"JAKE LORENZO, THE WORLD'S ONLY 100 POINT WINE WRITER. HELL, MAKE IT 110 POINTS"

Larry Walker, *author of Wines of the Napa Valley*

"In the wonderful, but complex world of wine, there is nobody like Jake Lorenzo. Nobody. He is our Henry Miller, our Paul Gauguin, our Robin Williams."

Bob Sessions, *Winemaker Emeritus Hanzell Vineyards*

"Nietzche borrowed Dionysus to symbolize genius, the force that encourages each one of us to respond to the world freely, in his or her own way. If he'd waited a while, he'd have had a better example: Jake Lorenzo."

Gerald Asher, *Gourmet Magazine*

"Sherlock Holmes, Inspector Clouseau, Sam Spade and even Thomas Magnum can't hold a corkscrew to super wine detective Jake Lorenzo."

Lance Silver, *Winemaker Tobin James Winery*

"Jake Lorenzo's passion and curiosity about great wine hasn't waned despite decades of stomping grapes, bouncing barrels and dealing with distributors. His writing is as sublime and memorable as fine wine."

Cyril Penn, *Editor, Wine Business Monthly*

"Forget the *Wine Spectator*, *Wine Advocate* or any traditional wine publication. Jake Lorenzo has created the book for people who are into wine and just enjoy a good read."

Ray Kaufman, *Winemaker Laurel Glen Vineyards*

"Jake Lorenzo is the Phillip Marlowe of the wine business. Read this book and you'll never think the same way about wine again."

Mel Knox, *Knox Industries*

Continued Surveillance

Mostly True Stories of the Wine Business

by
Jake Lorenzo

WINE PATROL PRESS FIRST EDITION, MARCH 2010

Library of Congress Catalogue Number: 2009939360

Lorenzo, Jake. Continued Surveillance: Mostly True
Stories of the Wine Business
By Jake Lorenzo

—Second Edition
p.cm

ISBN 978-0-9825759-1-8
$17.95 Softcover

Published by
Wine Patrol Press
113 Fetters Ave.
Sonoma, CA 95476 USA

Printed in the United States of America

For cellar rats and wine salesmen:
the people who make it and the people who sell it.
Without you, there is no wine business.

ACKNOWLEDGEMENTS

Thanks to Scott Summers who contributed the cover and translated my work into good looking print. He was far and away the most straightforward computer technician it has been my pleasure to work with.

Frank Gaynor and the people at McNaughton Gunn, Inc. for their patience and competence regarding the printing of this book.

Wine Business Monthly for providing a monthly forum where Jake Lorenzo can vent, write and tell stories.

Thanks to all of the people who gave encouragement, advice, help and discounts in the editing, printing and publishing of this book.

Thanks to all of the patrons whose generous pre-paid purchase of *Continued Surveillance* raised the capital to proceed and gave life to this book.

Guests who have shared our table, helped to empty our wine cellar and stepped up whenever they were needed.

All of the Toonknockers, wherever they are.

Jerry, Catherine and Miss Sandy… Thanks for everything.

Contents

PART IV

WINEMAKING   109

PART V

FAMILY   151

PART VI

TRAVEL   179

PART I

A JAKE'S LIFE

Mid·life Crisis

Get What You Need

Early Retirement

Three·hour Lunch

Arrogance

Busted

Live Entertainment

Safety First

Things Change

Finance

Music in the Bottle

Public Service Announcement

Mid-Life Crisis

Captain Jon called to his first mate, "Cast off, Jake, we're headin' out." A gentle breeze slid along the water carrying the salty smell of fish and mud. The blue sky sparkled, cloud free. We motored out of the marina onto the Napa River. I popped the cork on a delightful Spanish Cava, and we toasted our maiden voyage on Phazetoo, Captain Jon's new boat.

Captain Jon was in the midst of a mid-life crisis, his second. Three years ago, he left his career as a consolidator. That was his first mid-life crisis. Consolidators and logistics people are truckers. You'd think winemakers would know all about this, but they can't be bothered. Winemakers get the wine orders, call the truckers, and then go out for a three-hour lunch. They must assume that their 112 cases of fancy wine will be hand carried to their distributor in Missouri, but it doesn't work that way.

Consolidators pick up all the small orders from wineries. They drive back to their warehouses, unload, stage the orders by distributor and delivery site, combine them with other orders and then pass them over to logistics. Logistics arranges for containers, loads them, trucks them to site, or passes them off to rail or ship to get to their destination. Consolidators work their asses off, have liability up the kazoo, and barely eke out a living. Logistics people also work their asses off, and they can make big bucks, but they can't survive without the consolidators.

Three years ago, logistics learned to survive without Captain Jon, because he was having his first mid-life crisis. He sold his business and all of his trucks. He resolved the various pending lawsuits, made sure his employees had jobs, and kissed 15 years of trucking goodbye.

Lucky for Jake Lorenzo, because after 23 years of renting a charming 840 square foot cottage, Jake had been tossed out. His landlords were selling, and

Jake couldn't afford to buy. I convinced Captain Jon to help me build my new house. "I've had plenty of mid-life crises," I told him. "Stick with me, I'll get you through this."

We worked side by side building a stunning 1,450 square foot home for less money than a lot of people spend stocking their wine cellars with over-priced Napa Valley Cabernets. From start to finish, it took four months, a record in Sonoma County. The house features bamboo floors, a fireplace, gorgeous tile work, and a large working kitchen. Basically, it is a party house, a house for entertaining, and that's what we do three or four nights a week.

Captain Jon was so good at helping to build my house that a lot of my friends started hiring him to work on theirs. For the past three years he's been remodeling, tiling, plumbing, wiring, and painting houses in the valley. He hates it. That's why he had his second mid-life crisis.

Me, I've had plenty of mid-life crises. Jake Lorenzo looks forward to them, sort of forced career changes. Back in the seventies, I was a teacher. Teaching got me into drinking, and drinking led to the private eye business. By 1980 I was head of security for the San Francisco 49ers. They fired me after I shot a fan. Of course the fan was drunk, half-naked, had clubbed one of my security guards with a pipe wrench, and I just grazed his leg enough to subdue him. I thought I'd get a medal, but I got the mid-life crisis instead.

I was a detective in Sonoma, so I focused on high society murder cases. Unfortunately, Sonoma has no high society, and rarely does anyone get murdered. I survived working for various winery owners who hired me to catch their spouses in compromising positions. Once I got the goods for an employer, the winery owners would try to stiff me. (It was the eighties after all.) Rather than get nothing, I'd take part of my fee in wine. (They couldn't sell the stuff anyway.) I became a wine expert, which led to becoming a wine writer.

I've lived in Sonoma for 27 years now. I raised a daughter, Jakelyn who married and has just had her second child. I live in my new house with Jakelyn's mother who used to be a weaver. She took a job running a tasting room at a very prestigious local winery, and she must have been pretty good because she had that job for 17 years. Then she had her mid-life crisis and got into gardening. That mid-life crisis almost killed Jake Lorenzo. Hauling topsoil, dragging rocks, pulling weeds and shoveling gravel can wear out a detective.

We've got lots of friends, maybe because we wine and dine them often. My best friend is Chuy Palacios who owns Chuy's Burrito Palace, Sonoma's finest restaurant, hands down. He won't let me talk about it anymore, because he hates it when tourists go there. Chuy acts like he's having a perpetual mid-life crisis, but that's just the way he is.

I drink wine everyday. Jakelyn's mom is right there with me. We have our prejudices. First off, we prefer red wine, although we will drink some whites. We love dry Gewürztraminers if they are crisp and spicy. Sauvignon blanc can be delicious, and a glass of sparkling wine seems the perfect starter on a warm spring day sitting on our porch looking a Jakelyn's mom's garden.

Given a choice, we'll almost always go for Pinot Noir. It's so hard to make a consistently good Pinot Noir, and the delicate complexities of the varietal please us in a soul satisfying way. Cabernet and Syrah are favorites, and we drink Zins with barbecue, but wish they weren't so high in alcohol with those overripe hints of VA.

We're working people with very limited income, so we're always looking for good wine at fair prices. Right now, that means we're drinking mostly foreign like Spanish wines from Jumilla, Alicante, and Borja. We drink lots of Cotes du Rhone, but not the rain vintage of 2002. We're suckers for Italian Rosso di Montalcinos ever since our last visit to Tuscany. We have pretty good luck with Torrontes and Malbec from Argentina.

When it comes to wine, there is no such thing as a mid-life crisis at Jake Lorenzo's house. My theory is drink good, drink often, and drink plenty. In case of an emergency, start with the oldest vintages first.

When we were building the house, Captain Jon would come over for dinner often. He can't get enough of Jakelyn's mom's croutons. (By the way Pinot Noir goes best with her croutons.) At one of those dinners I broached the subject of Captain Jon's pants. He doesn't wear them, at least not long ones. I've known Captain Jon for more than 12 years and I've never seen him in long pants, not once. As a private eye, I've got to wonder, "What childhood trauma is so hurtful that a man has to go through the rest of his life with naked knees."

Well, Captain Jon isn't talking so we'll probably never know. One thing I do know is his second mid-life crisis is a good one. He's given up construction work. He locked his tools into a container stored over at Ronnie Groskopf's, and he has started Wine Country Yacht Charters. He and his first mate, Jake Lorenzo, take tourists out on his classic 42-foot yacht. We cruise up the Napa River or down to the bay. Occasionally we'll go look at the moth ball fleet. It's totally relaxing. Captain Jon serves wonderful wine, delicious, inventive food, and he looks perfectly at home in shorts.

Personally, my latest mid-life crisis has caused me to branch out in my writing career. Health insurance keeps going up, and I'd hate to get a real job. So, here I am writing for *Wine Business Monthly*. They say I can write about anything that strikes my fancy, and they don't mind if I wear shorts.

Get What You Need

You don't need a private eye like Jake Lorenzo to tell you the obvious. My job is to find the hidden agenda, the man behind the mask, the truth behind the lie. And we'll get to that soon enough, but it's one of those obvious observations that have inspired this column.

There's a world of difference between what you need and what you want. Even the Rolling Stones figured this out, and they did it at a time when there wasn't much wanting they couldn't have. Jake Lorenzo wants a new truck. My 18 year-old Ford Ranger keeps running worse and worse. Now it is powered by "devil acceleration." Step on the gas pedal in my truck and sometimes you get nothing. No acceleration. No movement, just a long drawn out vehicle stutter. This is a good way to die, if the stutter occurs as you are trying to breech the endless speeding line of cars on Highway 12.

To tell the truth I could live with a stuttering vehicle, but sometimes that same truck accelerates like Jeff Gordon at Sears Point Raceway, *without* Jake Lorenzo doing anything. The engine screams and whines pegging the tachometer (if I had one) in the danger zone, and my foot's not even on the accelerator. This wouldn't be so bad, but when the "devil acceleration" is churning, I can't shift the gears. Next thing you know the truck is flying along at 40 miles per hour, *in first gear*.

So Jake Lorenzo's truck has a mind of its own. Sometimes it goes really fast and sometimes it won't go at all. It keeps this detective sharp and aware when he's behind the wheel. If you see me driving around town, it would behoove you to keep your distance. That's why Jake wants a new truck, but the damn thing keeps running, and Jake Lorenzo is short of financial wherewithal so a new truck is not something I need.

A truck with a mind of its own is a little like being married. Those of you who have experienced wedded bliss know that your spouse certainly has a mind of their own. You've got no more chance of figuring out that mind than Jake Lorenzo has of figuring out his truck.

Jake Lorenzo *needs* to travel. I've got places to go, friends to see, food to eat and wine to drink. Travel feeds my soul. Jakelyn's mother wants to go back to Europe. Unfortunately, the dollar isn't doing so well against the Euro. Hand them 100 dollars in Europe, and you are lucky to get 70 Euros back. That's a hell of a loss just to switch the color of money, especially for a financially challenged guy keeping an 18 year-old truck powered by "devil acceleration."

It's a drag to not get what you want. Jakelyn's mother was not happy about missing a trip to Europe. I showed her tickets to New Orleans (Europe in America.) I showed her tickets to Mexico for February (a lovely beach in the warm sun in a country that gives us 11 Pesos for each dollar.) I promised a trip to Nicaragua or Argentina for later in the year. Our needs will be met. It just requires some creative substitution.

That Euro thing is raising havoc with the wine business. After the grapes, the most important taste factor in wine is the oak used in aging. French oak, given the current exchange rate, is pushing $800 for each barrel. Winemakers want French oak barrels in just the way Jakelyn's mother wants to go back to Europe. Winery owners and accountants sit those winemakers down and explain to them that they are not going to get all those French oak barrels while they are $800 apiece. They advise some creative substitution.

When it comes to oak, creative substitution has been around for a long time. Until recently it hasn't tasted too good. But now winemakers can choose between a myriad of oak integration systems based on forms like oak beans, oak staves, oak sleeves, oak chains and oak blocks. These alternatives to oak barrels are much more effective thanks to micro-oxygenation technology, which involves the controlled introduction of oxygen into wine over a short period of time. In some instances micro-oxygenation, in conjunction with oak substitutes, produces wines equal in quality and flavor profiles as those aged in oak barrels.

If Jake Lorenzo can talk Jakelyn's mother out of her European vacation in exchange for one to New Orleans, Mexico and Nicaragua, then believe me, it won't take much for those winery owners and accountants to talk their winemakers out of $800 French oak barrels. In fact, since Jake Lorenzo is a detective, he happens to know that this has been going on in the wine business for quite some time.

According to a *Wine Business Insider* survey, 86 percent of large wineries are already using micro-oxygenation and 45 percent of mid-size wineries use it. Every large winery that responded to their survey is already using "barrel alternatives" and so are 53 percent of small wineries. Close to 75 percent of all wineries report that they expect an increase in the use of barrel alternatives.

What Jake Lorenzo, private eye, wants to know is why are all of these winemakers afraid to talk about what they are doing? It's not like you are putting glycol into your white wines, or that you're making tequila with absolutely no agave. It's not like you're part of the vigilante group that's taken out a contract on Jim Laube, or that you've re-labeled Chilean Cabernet as Napa Valley's finest.

When the fine wine business got started in the late seventies, most wine consumers didn't even know wine was aged in oak barrels. Hell, most winemakers didn't know. We educated them about the barrels, the forests, and the toast levels. Wine consumers love to be in the know. They like to think they are on the cutting edge. Tell them all about micro-oxygenation. Tell them about your oak beans, sleeves and blocks. Let them in on the secret. Get them involved in the excitement. Then show them the savings.

Oak barrels have always been expensive. They make the wine taste great, but they cost a lot of money. Oak integration systems have been proven to produce wonderful wines. Wineries have been selling them, and consumers have been drinking them for years. Oak integration systems cost less than oak barrels. A lot less. Pass this savings on to the consumers and they will love you. They will come to love micro-oxygenation and they will treasure oak barrel alternatives.

If you give the wine drinking public a bottle of wine that tastes good, has varietal character, some acid balance, a moderate amount of oak flavor and sell it for a reasonable price, then the public will champion you and support you by buying thousands of cases of your wine.

Take it from a detective, secrets are nasty. It's almost impossible to keep a secret, especially one that everyone already knows about. When it comes to oak integration systems, there is nothing to be ashamed of. It's new technology. It's economic sense. Tell the truth. It will set you free.

Early Retirement

Very few people end up being what they started off to become. Lucky for the California wine business, because it wouldn't exist, as we know it were it not for people who started off as something else.

Jim Bundschu sold Sonoma real estate. Cecil De Loach used to be a fireman. Larry Turley worked triage in emergency rooms. Patrick Campbell coaxed notes from his violin for the symphony. All of them got into the wine business in the 1970's, and each in a different way contributed to the modern California wine industry.

Doctors (Hanna, Mazocco, Roach), dentists (Philip Staley, Pete Minor), developers (Haywood, Ledson) and lawyers (Jess Jackson, Ferrari Carano, Fred Firth at Chalk Hill) all moved into the world of wine. Movie directors (Coppola), television stars (Fess Parker), screenwriters (Robert Kamen) and even ballet dancers (Rodney Strong) all got seduced by the wine business. Sports heroes as revered as Joe Montana, Tom Seaver and Rusty Staub have all retired to afternoons in the vineyards and evenings making fine wines. The wine world even attracted its own contingent of surfers (Bill Hawley at Random Ridge, Oded Shakked at J.)

I don't know the personal history of a lot of California winemakers. I think it's more fun to guess. Randall Grahm could easily have worked at or been an inmate of an asylum in France. Warren Winiarski probably toiled for years as a writer for the *Dictionary of Aphorisms*. Bob Sessions may well have been a stand-in for Gary Cooper in *High Noon*.

The point is all of these people trained for, worked at, and were successful doing something else. Then they chucked it all aside, or retired from that calling, or used it to finance their way into the wine business. The modern wine industry is built upon the lives of people fleeing from jobs they couldn't abide, or leaving jobs which they no longer found challenging.

Jake Lorenzo understands this evolution. I mean I never started out to be a private eye. Hell no. When I was a kid, I wanted to play guard for the Lakers, play second base for the Giants, and be the setter for Al Skates' UCLA volleyball team. I settled for head of security for the 49ers.

In college, I wanted to end the war in Vietnam, integrate the South with Martin Luther King, play the bass like Ray Brown and live on a giant organic commune that raised mangos. I settled for several years as a teacher in East L.A., a record collection, and a garden in my backyard. Even after a successful career as a high-profile detective, I moved into wine writing, book publishing and house building.

Most people do this. Chuy Palacios was a lawyer before he opened the Burrito Palace. Iggy Calamari rented shoes in a bowling alley before he became a world famous researcher. Jakelyn's mother was a weaver before she developed the prettiest garden in Fetters Hot Springs.

Hardly anyone sets out to do something and sticks with it for a lifetime, and that's what got Jake Lorenzo thinking. For the past ten to twenty years the wine business has attracted people who want to be in the wine business. They go to UC Davis, UC Fresno, or even Cornell to learn about wine. They come to wine country seeking jobs in the wine industry. Hundreds of our winemakers, lab managers and cellar rats have known nothing other than their jobs in the wine industry.

If they are anything like the rest of the people in the United States, they are getting ready to move on. It's a simple matter of evolution. I can see where doctors, lawyers, burnt-out business executives and retired athletes would find the wine business charming. Working with Mother Nature in idyllic settings and getting high on fine wine sounds like Shangrila after fighting rush hour traffic to work 9 to 5 for some heartless corporation whose only concern is the bottom line.

For those who dreamed about getting into the wine business, those who have lived it as their only job, the romantic notions of the business don't exist. There's a lot of pressure in the wine business these days. Things are very competitive. The vineyard has to be state-of-the-art, or organic, or biodynamic. The winery has to be garagiste, a showplace, or funky with inestimable charm. The wines have to be extracted, complex, balanced, delicious, and sell for astronomical sums of money. You've got to have tasting rooms, wine clubs, sales managers, brokers and distributors. You worry about stuck fermentations, brettanamyces infection, TCA, VA and limp rubber hose disease. Don't forget the bankers, the public relations, BATF, ABC, and the wine writers. Then there's the bottom line of the wine business always and forever: making wine is hard, dirty, physical work.

If the wine business has become more about business than wine, then the people in the wine business are soon to start looking for something better. If you are in the wine business and this column is tickling your brain waves with obvious signs of recognition. If you're thinking, "Jake Lorenzo is a mind reader, and how does he know these things about me?" then you need the next better thing.

Jake Lorenzo knows what that better thing is. The next best thing is early retirement. Only by giving up work completely can we avoid moving to some job that will eventually turn into the same old nightmare of stress and pressure. It doesn't matter how old you are or how long you've worked. It doesn't matter how much money you've saved. It doesn't matter if you have four kids to put through college. Early retirement is the next big thing, and you'd better get in on the ground floor.

Jake Lorenzo hasn't had a real paying job for 8 years. I've managed to build a brand new house, travel 6–8 weeks every year, and eat fine food and drink delicious wines most every night. I've got no big bank account and no secret source of income. I am a master of early retirement.

I will teach you how to do it, but I'm not giving away my secrets for free. Hire Jake Lorenzo as your Personal Early Retirement Trainer. There are no guarantees, but what have you got to lose? If all else fails, you can always get a job in the wine business.

Three-hour Lunch

After four frigid days in Seattle visiting Jakelyn and the grandkids, Jake Lorenzo returned home to a solid week of miserable weather. Steady, unrelenting rain punctuated by titanic cloud bursts and stiff winds made it impractical to work outside. My Mexican beach vacation tan had long since faded. The false spring of February was a faint memory. I was caught up on all my indoor work, so I decided to go to lunch.

Of all the things the wine business has given us, is there anything better on a cold, rainy afternoon than a three-hour lunch? Not to my way of thinking.

The hardest part of setting up a three-hour lunch is finding people who have three hours to spend. Since most people insist on working for a living, they have ready-made excuses for declining lunch invitations: "Jake, I'd love to, but I've got to test 28 batches of corks to make sure there's no TCA." "Jake, I wish I could, but we're having a meeting to see how high we can raise our prices this year." "Jake, I'll have to take a rain-check, we've got a major inventory on the library wines coming up."

Nowadays, too many people think they are indispensable. They convince themselves that things won't work if they are not on site supervising. One thing that Jake Lorenzo knows for certain is that no one is indispensable. One way or another everyone can be replaced, and eventually you will be. Keep that in mind the next time you back out of an invitation and continue to horde your vacation days. Every job comes with its stresses including the wine business. Why wait for all that stress to give you a physical ailment? Why not use some of that sick leave for mental health? If it makes you feel better, you can go to work in the morning and put in a half day before you go to lunch, but don't even think of going back to work.

Way back when I actually had a job, I'd always confound my bosses at salary negotiations. I'd accept smaller raises. I'd low-ball the bonuses, but I was adamant about getting more time off, and once I got it, I'd use it. Jake Lorenzo never left an hour of sick leave or vacation on the table. I never turned down an invitation to an interesting afternoon lunch either.

A three-hour lunch is like a holiday, and while there's plenty to be said about picking the restaurant, deciding on menu items and determining the number of courses, the real key is the wine. Nothing is better at letting loose the tongue and the sense of humor and wicked sarcasm. No other beverage matches with fine food as well, offers so much variety to choose from and allows you to imbibe for several hours without getting loaded.

There's a reason wine and food are so perfectly matched. After all, chefs and winemakers have similar jobs. Both need to work with fresh, perfectly ripened ingredients. They both need to work those ingredients into something unique and delicious. They both need to inspire their crews to work as a team, and they both put their wares out to the public and get instant feedback. They understand how much work is involved in doing the job right, and they appreciate how fragile and rare success can be.

When someone in the wine business sits down to a serious lunch, especially at a local restaurant, there should be an immediate stirring in the kitchen, as the chef realizes he has the opportunity to showcase his talents for an appreciative audience. Usually a complimentary appetizer or two will appear. This is great so long as the chef doesn't overdo it. After all, one of the joys of a three-hour lunch is slowly working your way around the menu and the specials to arrive at the perfect food combinations. Too many complementary dishes and you're too full to order what you wanted in the first place.

On these special lunch occasions, I approach the wine just like food at a Chinese restaurant. Each person brings or picks a bottle, and then we order one more for the table. It gives each person the chance to show something of interest. It causes all of us to concentrate on ordering appropriate food for the various wines, and it insures that we won't go thirsty.

It's just a personal thing, but Jake Lorenzo is not big on getting new wine glasses for each and every bottle opened. It just seems like so much ruckus and there's never enough room. I figure I'm a professional, so just two wine glasses works for me. I do not want my glasses over-filled, nor do I want all the food showing up at the same time. The whole idea is to have a long, slow dining experience while getting sweetly juiced on some fine wines. So, if the kitchen is cranking the food out too quickly, it is imperative to slow them down.

The secret to the three-hour lunch is attitude. Decide that you are going to have a great time with your friends, the food and the wine. Don't let little things bother you. If the wine list is priced like jewelry at Cartier's, just root around until you find the best bargains available and expect to leave a WinePAL* card or two to let them know you won't be back until they get with the program.

Jake Lorenzo is a great believer in talking to your server. It's something I learned in New Orleans. If you can't decide between the Crabmeat Maison and the Shrimp Remoulade, ask if they will give you a half and half order. Servers and restaurants shrewd enough to accommodate their customers will likely serve great food. Always ask if there are any specials for the day, and insert a question or two to break up their rote presentation. Always ask if the chef is fixing things that no one knows about, especially in Italian restaurants. Never ask a waiter what he or she would recommend. After all, the server is an unknown commodity. They could be vegans or teetotalers for all you know.

Once you've ordered, sit back and enjoy what the chef is doing for you. Converse with your friends. Sip your wines. Try to laugh a lot. Let your server taste the wines. Invite friends to stop by your table. Let the wine bottles pile up, and become your own exhibit to the joys of wine in the afternoon.

Wine is one of the great stress-relievers in the history of man. Those of us who make it, need to assure ourselves of its healing properties more often. Invite some friends to lunch and take the rest of the day off. You'll have a great time. If you can't find enough guests for your own lunch, and you're on an expense account, give Jake Lorenzo a call.

*WinePAL (Wine Patrol Approved List) is a program that requires restaurants to have at least one bottle in each category under $30, and to have at least 10 percent of the total wine list under $30. For more information about how you can help see www.winepatrol.com.

Arrogance

Last month Jake Lorenzo and Jakelyn's mom were on our way to New Orleans. We disembarked from the shuttle and made our way to the skycaps to check our luggage. We like using the skycap service. They usually seem friendlier and less harried than their counterparts inside, and we've never had our luggage disappear when a skycap has taken it under his wing.

The skycap pointed to a United Airlines sign that read, "$2.00 per bag service charge." "That's a bit presumptuous on their part," I thought, "but $2.00 per bag is okay with me."

The skycap explained, "The $2.00 is for the airline. None of that comes to me."

Now that pissed me off. They want to charge for your luggage and then have you tip on top of that. Most people aren't going for that, and I watched as several dragged their luggage inside to wait in line at the ticket counter, instead of dealing with the skycap and the new charges. Clearly United Airlines is trying to put the skycaps out of business. I know that United Airlines is having some rough times, but the arrogance of undermining your own employees and their ability to earn a living is reprehensible.

Jake Lorenzo has lived in Wine Country for 30 years. People are always asking me what it used to be like and how it has changed. That recent encounter at the airport clarified the whole thing for me. Wine Country has become arrogant.

When I first moved here in 1977, Sonoma typified the small farming community. Work was hard and the pay was low. Rent was cheap. Locals ran the roost, and tourists were scarce. Hotels were non-existent. Motels were shabby and well-used. There was little traffic, one stoplight in the entire valley and everything closed up by nine o'clock.

Arrogance

Restaurants followed the family dining format: usually large Italian meals that started with antipasto, followed by salad, soup and pasta before your entrée. Dessert and coffee were always included. Cocktails were cheap. Wine was limited to White, Rosé, Red and a few inexpensive examples from local producers. There were less than 50 wineries in the whole county.

Going to wineries to taste their wines was an adventure. Tasters were welcomed like long-lost relatives. Wines flowed freely with servers and tasters equally excited by the flavors and complexities to be found in the bottle. Servers willingly shared information with their guests, talked about winemaking techniques, barrel types and the weather.

As wine got better and more people discovered the charms of Wine Country, restaurants opened to serve the tourists. The chefs embraced local products including the wine. The motels cleaned themselves up and business boomed. Shops opened up to sell whatever shops sell. But everyone realized we were serving these tourists, treating them to a look at our glorious home territory. Waiters, shop-keepers, tasting room servers, even winemakers were polite, friendly and pleasant to all of these acolytes of the new California wine industry.

Wine may have attracted the tourists to Wine Country, but what kept them coming back was the friendly service. It reminded all the city dwellers in their hustle-bustle lives that alternatives existed. Tourists would stand in the bakery and watch the locals exchange pleasantries, talk about the kids, and the high school baseball team. They'd sit in front of the Swiss Hotel on a warm summer evening and listen to the locals sing songs and drink Ghalarifies. They linked that warm, rural personality to the wines, and they bought cases of the reasonably priced wine. Returning home to their busy lives, they could remind themselves of the slow-paced Wine Country lifestyle every time they opened a bottle.

Recently, six friends came to stay with us for a week. Jake Lorenzo called a local restaurant for reservations. "Can't seat eight, sorry," said the girl answering the phone even though I was giving her a month's notice. "The only way you might get in is to talk to the manager. I'll have him call you."

Of course, the manager never called back. When I called him, he said, "Maybe I could squeeze you in at six o'clock. Let me check with Chef and get back to you." We never heard from him, and we're locals. How do you think the tourists are getting treated?

Hotels abound in Wine Country now, but there aren't many bargains. Rooms are pricey and the rates go up on weekends. Try to bring a group, and they insist you let them cater an event or the rooms suddenly become unavailable.

Restaurants offer all kinds of fine dining. Want to split an entrée? There's an extra charge. Wine by the glass starts at $6 and proceeds quickly to $12 and up. Wine list prices average $40 to $50 per bottle, and even if you buy a bottle off the list they still charge corkage for that special birthday or anniversary bottle you brought from home. Hell, last week at a local restaurant, a bus boy asked me to pass him my plate and then came back and asked me to collect up the silverware.

Winery tasting rooms are less about wine and more about sales. Shirts, hats, corkscrews, dishes, bags, and kitchen sinks. The servers have the enthusiasm of dirt and answer questions with the drone-like inflection of automated answering machines. Five bucks just to taste and constant pressure to join the wine club doesn't sound hospitable to Jake Lorenzo.

Hotels, restaurants and wineries all have customers. That means hotels, restaurants and wineries are part of the service industry. We are supposed to provide service. That's our primary job. Keep telling those customers, "It's our way or the highway," and they'll move on down the road. Keep treating them like your own personal ATM machines, and they'll move their pin codes to another jurisdiction. Keep your arrogant attitude, your lackadaisical service and your haughty wine savvy on display, and the tourists will migrate somewhere else to spend their dollars.

Good service is easy. Just listen to the customer, and then give him what he wants. From the top management to the lowliest worker, it's the job of everyone in a service industry to please the customer.

Service industries that abandon good service are destined to fail, and the fall is quick and brutal. Ask United Airlines. Business always tries to save itself before it worries about its employees. Ask the pilots, stewards and ground crew about their pension plan. Ask a United skycap how he's doing now that the airline is charging to check bags curbside.

Busted

D r. Iggy Calamari sat by himself in the corner booth of the Burrito Palace. Sobs racked his willowy frame and he frequently dabbed tears from his eyes with a paper napkin stained with Chuy's Huevos Rancheros sauce.

Jake held out his coffee mug for a refill. Chuy poured in a shot of Centinela Reposada tequila and then filled the cup with his steaming Oaxacan coffee blend. "What's up with the good doctor," asked Jake, glancing toward Calamari.

"It's the stock market, Jake. Iggy says he's been wiped out, that an entire lifetime of hard work has disappeared overnight in this economic collapse." Chuy waited for Jake's reply.

Jake sipped his coffee, sneered in Calamari's direction. "What, he thinks the residuals for his wine powered pacemaker are in jeopardy? If anything, this crash will give so many people heart attacks that he'll make even more money than before. He's being a baby, and I'm disgusted by his infantile behavior."

Chuy shook his head in agreement. "I'm with you carnal. It's not like he's the only one affected. Everyone is taking a hit on this one."

"You know who's making a lot of money?" asked Jake. "The government printers. Those poor bastards must be working 24/7 on the presses printing money as fast as they can. They must be making double and triple time. It's not like the government had $700 billion lying around in some cupboard. They have to print all that bailout money and that's a lot of press time."

"Yeah," Chuy laughed, "but no matter how fast they print it, the money is worth less and less. They'll be lucky to catch up." He poured another slug of tequila into his coffee and shuffled off into the kitchen to continue with the breakfast rush.

Economics are not my strong suit, and frankly money is not the end all and be all for this detective. Being a private eye doesn't pay all that well, but Jake Lorenzo and Jakelyn's mom never bought into spending on credit. We're very much "pay as you go" people. We learned to live very well without fancy cars, boats, vacation homes and dining in hip restaurants. We spent what we needed to live, but we never spent more than we had on extra stuff. Most Americans have way more than they need, so much that we can't fit it into our houses and garages, so we rent extra space to store all the stuff that we own but never use.

We have a beautiful home, but we built it simply and saved a ton by doing most of the work ourselves. We travel two or three months a year, but we schedule our trips around airfare deals and make excellent use of our accumulated miles. We entertain often with great meals and fine wine, but we grow most of our own vegetables, make our own wine and do the bulk of our entertaining in our own kitchen.

Jake Lorenzo hates to see anyone suffer, but this whole stock market/banking fiasco serves us right. Finally, people may start to understand what Jake Lorenzo has spent years railing about. The wine business in particular is in for a rude awakening.

We've done a great job getting people to like and drink wine, but our prices, especially in restaurants are ridiculous. In hard times people need to drink, and they might as well drink wine, but when you lose 30 to 40 percent of your holdings, it makes you reluctant to continue purchasing $50 bottles of middling California wine. People looking for ways to cut expenses are going to figure out that those monthly wine club selections arriving at the front door aren't a necessity anymore.

Taking trips to Wine Country to visit wineries that charge $20 and up for the privilege of tasting their wines don't sound like fun when your IRA account is leaking faster than an oak barrel infested with barrel borers. The snooty indifference of the service staff at all those Wine Country shops, hotels and restaurants will stick in tourist craws worse than too-dry must in a minestrine hose.

In the housing market people bought houses way beyond their means. They used no down-payments, interest only loans and adjustable rate mortgages to climb into the market. Houses were appreciating so fast, people figured if worse came to worse, they'd sell the house and be fine. When the crash came, people found they couldn't sell their houses for what they owed on them. Foreclosures escalated.

Years ago wineries started relying on direct sales to fatten their bottom line. They enlarged their tasting rooms, added merchandise to sell, started their wine clubs and gave out bonuses for hospitality staff when they signed up customers. Wine clubs and tasting room business grew so fast that wineries thought they had struck gold. They allocated more and more of their time and resources to direct sales and spent less and less time maintaining relationships with distributors and buyers in other cities and across the country. Over time they alienated distributors and out of state clients. Now, if the customers stop buying from the wine clubs and the tasting rooms, and they likely will, then wineries have a situation like the housing market.

Given the current economic situation, people are going to restaurants less. Fewer diners mean less wine sales. I suppose there are still some people with enough money to not care, but a whole lot more of us are going to start cutting corners. When I can go to a restaurant and have an appetizer, entrée and desert for under $40, but the cheapest bottle of wine I would consider drinking from the list is more than the price of my meal, then Jake Lorenzo says the wine corner is the one getting cut.

Retail sales are slumping. That means store owners will cut inventory. Less inventory translates into less wine sales. Like many people, I have a wine cellar full of wine. It's time to start drinking that up. Drinking through my wine cellar means I don't have to buy more wine. I can focus on what I already have.

Let's sum up: fewer people come to your tasting rooms; people flee your wine clubs; restaurant wine sales fall; retail sales shrink and you have no decent ongoing relationship with distributors or clients across the country. That sounds like a disaster to me.

Maybe you can sit around waiting for bailout money to trickle down from Wall Street to Main Street to Wine Country Avenue. Jake Lorenzo says you might want to take the offensive. Stop charging for tastings. Give 40 percent discounts to wine club members. Trade wine for food at restaurants. Give big discounts to retailers. Call your distributor, beg his forgiveness and get on a plane to meet the clients.

It may not be the right thing to get us through these hard times, but cheaper wine always lifts my spirits. What have we got to lose?

Live Entertainment

B ruce Campbell, the owner of CK Lamb is one hard working guy. He's up early, supervising the raising of his lambs. He does a lot of the butchering, deliveries and even most of the sales. That his product sells at Wolfgang Puck's restaurants and dozens of other high-end, hip, popular places is testament to Bruce's hard work and unstinting dedication to quality.

Bruce Campbell is no dilettante. He is not swayed by his brushes with celebrity. Bruce remains a Wine Country farmer. Jake Lorenzo is no dilettante either, and I'm certainly no Wolfgang Puck, but I am a customer of CK Lamb. In fact, it's the only lamb that we've used in our household for the past 22 years. In our mind, it is some of the finest lamb the world has to offer.

Bruce breaks down his lambs in a small shop in Santa Rosa. Basically, he rents space there for his operation. Most of the rest of the shop breaks down cows. Every now and then, a prime rib of such high quality comes down the line that the guys ask Bruce if he wants it. (Jake Lorenzo has no idea what comprises a special high-quality prime rib, but I respect the fact that there are people out there who do.) When he has the time, Bruce hangs those prime ribs, dry-ages them for 30 days and saves them for special occasions. On four scrumptious evenings, those occasions have been at our house.

A 15 pound, 30-day dry-aged prime rib is not a simple piece of meat. It requires 15 to 20 meat-eating, red wine-drinking, Yorkshire pudding-loving participants. It demands moving furniture, setting up tables, and boxes of wine glasses. It means Jakelyn's mother will clean the house, cut flowers from the garden and break out the fancy tablecloths and the fine cutlery.

A prime rib dinner at Jake Lorenzo's house assures that we'll be drinking out of magnums, maybe even a three-liter or two. It guarantees that we'll be up past 3 AM, but will find ourselves too full to partake of the late-night offerings from the burrito wagon. We'll surely find our way into the hot tub, and we'll awaken late the next morning to a houseful of guests.

For this particular feast, Jakelyn's mother had a surprise. We had spent three wonderful hours at table. The paté appetizer was delicious, as were the fresh, crispy-coated sardines served as a first course. The prime rib was fork-tender bursting with rich beef flavor. Chuy's Yorkshire pudding and roasted vegetables provided perfect colorful accompaniment. The fresh green salad from our garden worked perfectly with the St. Andre, and our guests were settling in for a comfortable evening of wine drinking and discussion and laughter.

We disrupted them when we insisted on breaking down one of the dinner tables at that very minute. "We haven't even had desert," someone protested. The back door opened and two friends walked in with guitars, speakers and amplifiers. In less than ten minutes they were seated, drinking cold beers and playing live music. Our guests were enthralled. Jakelyn's mother beamed. The musicians were talented, engaging, funny and entertaining.

Sitting in my own house, with a group of close friends, listening to live music proved a revelation to Jake Lorenzo. I remembered that for centuries, before the advent of television, stereos and video games, people socialized with artists. Musicians were entertainers, not just in concerts, but in people's homes. Actors performed not only in grandiose plays on stage, but in small vignettes in private parlors. Comedy clubs didn't start in bars, but in houses, after dinner.

We often forget that we are surrounded by talented people. Our lives move so fast, that it is easy to pigeonhole or categorize those we meet. He's the grocery clerk. She's the doctor. There goes our car mechanic. It never occurs to us that everyone is multifaceted. That hair dresser may be a fantastic opera singer. Even good friends can have hidden talents. Chuy Palacios plays smokin' blues harp. Iggy Calamari can juggle two bottles of wine, a bottle opener and a copy of *Wine Business Monthly* all at the same time.

As winemakers, we are always trying to get people to make wine a part of their life. What if wine is not conducive to the way we live our modern lives?

When Jake Lorenzo looks around to see the shrill insistence of cell phones, the constant pressure of the bottom line and the diminishment of the family dining experience, I have to think that wine may be more of an antidote to, rather than a natural part of, our daily lives.

Jake Lorenzo is no doctor. While wine may be medicine for the soul, it shouldn't be prescribed as some anesthesia against the buffeting of daily living. Wine's been around for hundreds of years. If it doesn't fit into our modern lives, then maybe it is time to change the way we live those lives.

Jakelyn's mom and I have decided to pursue this entertainment angle. We will have small dinner parties, even if they are potluck affairs. At each event we will have live entertainment. We'll have a couple of actors performing scenes from Shakespeare. We'll sponsor our own private Comedy Club one night. A poetry reading, a piano player, a juggler or even a lecturer on an interesting topic could be the cornerstone of a delightful evening.

Turn off the television. Turn off the stereo. Shut down the video games. Deaden the cell phones. Pull some corks. Eat some food. Spend time with friends and partake of live entertainment. Not only will you have fun, but you'll find out that all those people you encounter in your daily lives have talents, talents that can entertain you and your friends.

Get ten people over to the house and chip in $10 each. That's $100 you can pay the entertainment. Who wouldn't pay $10 for a private concert? Hell, at most venues, $10 won't even cover the parking. Get four or five people in your neighborhood to start regular, live entertainment soirees and you'll be providing thousands of dollars a year to the local entertainment industry. Entertainers are artists. Artists like wine. Their additional discretionary income means they can buy more wine. In the long run you'll be entertained and make more money.

There's another thing about live entertainment. Everyone likes it if it is good. Even kids. Drag your kids out from their bedrooms to watch the jazz duo in the living room. Have them watch a couple of scenes from Shakespeare in the back yard. Find out which of their friends entertain. Pay one of their friends to come and sing some original songs. Have the cheerleading squad perform their routines for a donation. Before you know it, your kids will be asking to have their friends over for their own dinner party.

What if wine and entertainment could forge an alliance to bring families closer together? I know it works with friends. Wine has always been part of our lives. From now on, live entertainment will be as well.

Safety First

By now, you all know how much Jake Lorenzo enjoys a great meal, especially when accompanied by good wine, lively conversation and fine company. I have written often and glowingly about the joys of the table. Alas, I must make amends.

Don't get me wrong, I still love eating and drinking with friends, but we all know that there's no such thing as a free lunch, and I would be less than honest if I didn't warn you of the very real dangers associated with certain aspects of the Wine Country lifestyle.

I'm not one of those detectives admonishing people to use moderation in all things. Hell, no. There's too much moderation in our lives. What we need is more passion, more letting it all hang out. But I just wouldn't feel right if I didn't warn you about the dangers lurking at the table and give you some safety tips to protect yourself when and if you launch into a Lorenzian binge of eating and drinking.

First off, you've got to pay attention to your blood pressure. The biggest blood pressure worry for Jake Lorenzo is walking into a restaurant and looking at the wine list prices. Nowadays, most lists start at $30 per bottle and escalate faster than HMO fees. It used to drive me crazy, and I'd sit figuring out how to organize hit squads to take out the creeps who were ruining my dining experience. For a while, I had good luck explaining to the waiter that I was under a doctor's care and shouldn't have any shocks to my system. Then when he handed me the list, I'd fall out of my chair, flop around on the floor and whimper something about the prices. Sometimes they'll comp you a bottle if make a big enough commotion.

Jakelyn's mom wasn't enamored of the "flop" technique, so she trained me to relax. Faced with one of those "screw you" wine lists, I've learned to see if they were clever enough to hide some treasures here and there. Not finding that, I peruse the Sauvignon Blancs or Gewürztraminers. Often they'll have reasonably priced sparkling wines, and in a pinch I can make do with that. If all else fails, it's fine to delve into the micro-brews. Under no circumstances should you acquiesce and pay those exorbitant prices. Doing so could lead to severe health problems, and having purchased a bottle or two you wouldn't have enough money to pay your doctor bills, would you?

Personally, I don't worry over my diet too much. I'm in pretty good shape and I still get a lot of exercise. When I get a batch of smoked boudin from Best Stop in Scott, Louisiana I slow-cook those babies on the grill, and I don't care how much fat is inside. If we finish a fine three-course meal and after drinking wine for a few hours decide to make a trip to the Burrito Wagon, I take my guests and introduce them to the delights of a chicharron gordita. If I'm sitting down to a table of fresh crawfish, you'll have to drag me away kicking and screaming until they are all gone.

On the other hand, once Jakelyn's mom and I were sitting on my porch with Jerry and Catherine Henry eating duck rillette and washing it down with fine burgundy as a precursor to a bottle of 1973 Chateau d'Yquem and a one-and-a-half pound foie gras. By the time we had consumed half of the foie gras, we could feel our blood slowing its flow through our veins. Had Ray Kaufman not shown up at exactly that time with a bottle of fine Champagne to lighten the load, to vaso-dilate our veins and to help finish the last of the foie gras; there's no telling what might have happened. To this day Jerry Henry claims that Ray saved our lives. All I'm saying is that it pays to be careful.

When it comes to drinking, I'm for it. Jake Lorenzo loves cocktails, beer and wine of all types and colors. (Well, maybe not pink, although I give it a try from time to time.) I love the pop of a cork, and if you're going to open a bottle of wine, why not open several? I like drinking wines in order: champagne, whites, reds and ports. I like drinking wines out of order, too. I like drinking verticals, horizontals and libraries. I like drinking foreign wines as well as domestic. I even love drinking expensive and famous wines if someone else is buying.

Of course, drinking bottle after bottle of wine night after night can tax your liver and lead to bloodshot eyes and throbbing heads. Take a lesson from the esteemed Dr, Iggy Calamari who told us, "The solution to pollution is dilution." Calamari is a doctor and he knows what he's talking about. We drink water. Loads of water. We drink tap water, filtered water, bottled water and fizzy water. Water keeps your palate fresh for that next bottle of wine. It dilutes the alcohol and flushes the kidneys, which means you have to go to the bathroom which means you are getting exercise and that means you are practicing good health.

When the evening is winding down, after the food and the wine, but before you hit the sack, it's time for the after-dinner drink. Jake Lorenzo has learned from years of experience that any after dinner drink means a headache the next morning for this detective. That doesn't stop me from partaking if the company is good and the liquor choices are varied. Whenever possible, for self preservation, I try to keep the after-dinner drinking to just one beverage. It's wonderful late-evening brain exercise to decide between a luscious Cognac, a peaty single malt, a rich earthy tequila or a smoky mezcal.

Sip the drink as if it were your last, because it should be.

Then fill up a glass of water and take it with you to bed. That way when you bolt upright in the bed with itchy eyeballs and cotton in your mouth, you'll be able to wash it away and go back to sleep. When you get up in the morning, lie in bed and see if you can remember each and every bottle you opened the night before. This recharges the brain cells and according to Dr. Calamari may help fight off Alzheimer's Disease.

Eating and drinking with friends can be a rewarding and pleasant activity provided you take the necessary precautions. First, protect your blood pressure by refusing to ever pay outrageous prices for wine. Second, have a safety net of friends who can come to your rescue with Champagne when needed. Third, the solution to pollution is dilution. Fourth, try to limit yourself to one after-dinner drink. Finally, get a good night's sleep.

These are not hard and fast rules, but they work for this detective/writer and my attorney (Chuy Palacios of the Burrito Palace) insisted I pass them along to you. So be it.

Things Change

Some things change and others don't. The weather has changed. Jake Lorenzo hasn't.

Thirty years ago, when we moved to Sonoma, summers were wonderful. The heat of the day would arrive around three to five in the afternoon, and while it occasionally reached 90 to 95° F, it always cooled down in the evenings. Then as now, we would likely have guests to dinner. Early evenings were comfortable and we'd wear shorts and shirts while sitting at the table on our porch sampling course after course and drinking bottle after bottle with our guests.

Typically by nine o'clock our guests would be shivering and begging for sweaters, jackets, scarves, thermal blankets or anything else we could find to keep the chill away. New Yorkers would cry with their nasally whine that it was colder than an unheated subway car in February. People from Colorado would tell us that snow was warmer than a summer night on our porch. Poor friends from Arizona, so used to sweltering summer nights, had to be lowered into our hot tub just to thaw out.

That's how it used to be in the summer in Sonoma. We'd have warm days with hot late afternoons, but most evenings were cold. Sure, we'd have the rare three-day heat wave and the nights would stay comfortable until later, but you could count those nights on the fingers of one hand.

Nowadays, that has all changed. We have triple digit temperatures at least 15 to 20 days every summer. Heat waves will often last six or seven days. It's as if the fog has something against Wine Country and won't come all the way up here from San Francisco anymore. (Maybe the fog doesn't like the sky-high wine prices or the $250 per night hotel rooms or the incredibly rude service, but Jake Lorenzo digresses.)

Things Change

Jakelyn's mother and I still have friends over for dinner. We often sit out on the porch having our multi-course dinners and our bottles of wine, but most nights we stay in our shorts and T-shirts as late as midnight. Half of the time, we can make our late-night run to the burrito wagon without jackets. Midwesterners delight in our warm evenings and low humidity. New Orleanians love sitting outside without being devoured by mosquitoes and gnats, but we locals know there is a price to pay.

The weather has definitely changed. It could be global warming or excess body heat from the ever growing world population or friction from the government printing presses as they make the money to pay for all of the bailouts, but things in Sonoma are getting warmer. In fact they often get downright hot.

When it's broiling outside and Jakelyn's mother's garden is wilting like a stressed Cabernet vineyard in a September heat wave, Jake Lorenzo says it is time to rearrange the wine cellar. At the old house my wine cellar was underneath the house. One wall was buried into the hillside and the temperature naturally stayed in the low sixties most of the summer. The new house, which is already approaching nine years old, sits on flat land and I had to build the wine cellar inside the house. I cool it with a simple wall air conditioning unit jerry-rigged to an external thermostat.

That wine cellar is one cool place to hang out on a scorching summer day. My inside cellar holds 60 cases. (I have another wine cellar outside in the garage.) At both ends of the cellar I have wall racks that hold rows of bottles stacked on top of one another. Each row handles six bottles, unless you try to stack those new fangled, ridiculous bottles that refuse to sit atop one another and insist on falling in crashing avalanches to break on the cellar floor.

I start with the wall racks. The short stacks, with just two or three bottles remaining, get moved over to the lay-down rack. Then I search through my cased wines, and fill in each row with six bottles of the same wine. The rows on the right hand side I fill with my homemade wines. Most are Pinot Noir and I try to place them in ascending order by vintage date. The rack on the left side is primarily for those commercial wines that I have found thrilling enough to justify purchasing full cases. When I finish, I'll stand back in the cool comfort of the wine cellar admiring the rainbow of shiny, bright capsule colors.

I have a long, floor-to-ceiling lay-down rack. It has six ten-foot long shelves and each one holds about 50 bottles. I've got sections for Italian, Spanish, French, Australian and ever-expanding Argentine wines. As I work my way through them, I find lost treasures and discover wines that need to be consumed sooner rather than later. Then I move on to the varietal rows. These rows are filled with California wines. One whole shelf is devoted to Pinot Noir. Others share Zinfandel, Merlot, Cabernet, blends and odds and ends like Tempranillo, Grenache and Sangiovese.

I work my way slowly through the rows arranging the bottles by variety and vintage date. I take note of duplicate bottles and older vintages, making mental notes about what we should drink up in the near future. I can't help myself. Certain wines make me think of meals I can prepare and friends I can invite to help consume them.

Thinking of specific meals reminds me to check the eclectic white wine section atop the right hand wall rack. Torrontes from Argentina, Gewürztraminer from Alsace, Pinot Grigio from Italy sit alongside Riesling from Australia, Sauvignon Blancs from New Zealand and California and even a nice selection of whites from Bulgaria. Atop the left hand wall rack I inventory the sparkling wines and check my dwindling Port supply.

It is leisurely, mindless work, this rearranging a wine cellar. Clanging the bottles, reading the labels, breaking down the emptied cardboard cases is simple, but on a sizzling summer day, working by the shadowy light in the cool room satisfies my soul. Jake Lorenzo takes solace in these unsure economic times, that baring some sort of natural disaster that wipes out my house, I have enough wine to get me through the rest of my life.

I take out an 11 year old Pinot Noir that I have found. I pull the cork. It is sound. I decant the wine noticing the beautiful, garnet color. I pour a taste into one of my 16-ounce wine glasses. The aroma is breath-taking; full of ripe fruits and dried violet with earthy spice. I taste the wine and it fills my mouth with rich, velvety textures and luscious dried fruit flavors. I marvel at the long finish as I refill my glass and pour another for Jakelyn's mother.

It doesn't matter how hot it is outside. There is something supremely satisfying in a good, perfectly aged bottle of wine from your own cellar. It's a reward for patience. When it comes to wine, that never changes.

Finance

When someone comes to Jake Lorenzo seeking professional help I ask them to take a seat, describe their problem and explain what they want me to do about it. If they seem sincere, and I think I can help them achieve their goals, I quote them a price, get a large cash advance and take on the job. We shake hands to seal the deal.

If, on the other hand, the prospective client strikes me the wrong way, lies to me, or plays me for a fool, then I tell him I'm swamped and can't take on any more cases. When some of the duller palookas try to muscle me, I give them a hard shin kick, then chop across the throat with the edge of my palm. I disarm them, and drag them gasping out into the hall. It matters not whether I take a case, refuse it or clear up a misunderstanding, the whole interaction is clean, straight-forward and simple.

Jake Lorenzo tries to avoid working lawyers at all costs. I can handle a few lawyers when they're not working. Some of them drink pretty good. Others have sail boats, and Jake always likes drinking on boats. I know a lawyer who has a small plane and will eagerly take me wherever I want to go just so he can fly. But put a lawyer on the clock and they lose all sense of humanity, morphing into dishonest, greedy leeches padding their billing hours and devising improbable scenarios so intricate that no one will ever understand them.

(Of course, my best friend, Chuy Palacios is a lawyer, but he's pretty much retired, doesn't charge for his services and makes a taco so sublime that tears come to your eyes when you take that first bite.)

Jake Lorenzo's been reading the wine news. Wine news has evolved through stages. First, we got stories of wineries and their struggle to make fine wine. Reporters questioned busy, blue-jeaned farmers and winemakers drawing out their dedication to growing wonderful fruit and making delicious wines. Photographers brought images of stunning vineyards and eerily romantic caves lined with row after row of barrels. From there we went to judgings, tastings and the hundred-point scale. We had years of stories about how healthy red wine was for our hearts. Then wine news labored over fine dining in expensive restaurants with extensive wine lists. Life style issues drove every story.

Currently, we're in the financial period of wine news. Sure people still use the 100 point scale, but no one cares unless you score above 90. There are still articles about dedicated winemakers, but we've already heard every version imaginable, so those stories play like reruns during the summer season.

Nowadays, wine news reads like the *Wall Street Journal.* I read about Pernod Ricard SA acquiring Allied Domecq for $14.2 billion. I follow the Foster's Group Ltd $2.5 billion offer for Southcorp Ltd. Global Wine Partners is putting together a vineyard REIT (Real Estate Investment Trust) and a separate private equity fund. I see where Joe Ciatti is offering a $159.4 million private offering through Vintage Wine Trust Inc. Beringer, Ravenswood and R.H Phillips, (after each had gone public), are gobbled up by larger organizations. Constellation Brands, Inc. buys Robert Mondavi, and Domaines Barons Rothschild privatizes Chalone Wine Group.

One thing for sure, all this buying and selling is creating a lot of work for lawyers, and you already know how Jake Lorenzo feels about lawyers. Hundreds of lawyers are on the clock giddily billing wineries for all sorts of arcane legal and financial issues. I envision lawyers hauling Hispanic workers off of tractors to give testimony before grand juries. I can see cellar rats dragged from crush pads to appear in court dockets wearing their rubber boots and raising their blackened wine-stained hands while swearing to tell the truth.

Think I'm exaggerating the consequences? Ever hear of Enron? You think Robert Mondavi survived splits with his brother, bitter in-fighting amongst his own family and forty years of cyclical wine business only to lose control of the business he started because some board of directors instructed their lawyers to get him out of the picture?

What the hell is going on here?

Private eyes don't know squat about the world of finance. I called Ken Macheras from Private Capital Management in Santa Rosa, California. Ken's the investment counselor who turned me on to the 72T early retirement program, thereby enabling me to pay for the new house I built a few years ago.

Macheras explained, "The wine industry has been an economic staple of California for decades. We're just witnessing the next phase of industry growth. The entire wine industry is going Wall St."

Macheras says that the wine business has enormous sex appeal to uneducated investors, and investors like to invest in goods that they actually use. Generally, winery stocks have under-performed against other stocks. Currently, there are too many dollars chasing too few assets, which is forcing them to pay too high a premium. In a business sense, prestige and reputation are not nearly as valuable as tangible assets like buildings, vineyard land and long-term grape contracts.

As big business gets a stronger hold on the wine industry, the industry will see the same tactics and consequences of takeovers as other businesses. "Large corporations," says Macheras, "will break off assets from an acquisition and sell them, especially if they will fetch large prices. A good example is Constellation Brands selling the high-end Mondavi properties like Arrowood and Byron to Legacy Estates. They likely will also lay off workers and force wineries to run leaner."

I still couldn't get a handle on why a guy like Robert Mondavi would take his company public and risk losing it. I can't imagine he needed the money. As Macheras continued on about IPOs and underwriters and prospectuses, I finally saw the light.

The guys designing IPOs stand to make a lot of money. They are salesmen. Family wineries don't go public just for money. They get sold a bill of goods. Imagine the salesman telling the winery owner, "You've got a beautiful life here in the country, doing honest labor, working with nature, making a product that helps keep people healthy. It's not fair to keep this to yourself. You need to share this 'Wine Country lifestyle' with the rest of the country. You'll do something for other people and you'll make enough money to never go hat in hand to banks again."

It's a pretty seductive notion for a farmer or winery owner, but ultimately deadly.

Successful corporate businesses know that dedication to quality will never replace the investor's need for earnings. The call will always be for bigger profits. Sooner or later the business interests will grab control of enough shares and then they'll throw the quality-minded farmer or winery owner out the door. "And take your 'Wine Country lifestyle' with you," they'll shout.

Jake Lorenzo likes things simple. Stocks, public offerings and corporate business all involve lawyers who are on the clock. Anything involving lawyers is not simple. If you are running a family winery, the only sure way to keep control is to never go public. You may get rich. You may go bust. Either way it will be your own doing. What's more challenging than that?

Music In The Bottle

Friday night was Chuy's annual secret concert. For eight years Chuy has hired a band, set up a venue, and put on a concert for Sonoma. Chuy looks upon the entire gig as his community service to wine country living. "Jake, it's my way of giving back to the community" he explains. "I just hate committee meetings, getting permits and dealing with bureaucrats. So, I prefer to do the whole thing myself."

The crowd is a heady mix of winemakers, cellar rats, vineyard growers and colorful local civilians. In most every way it is a delectable cross section of Wine Country population. The music each year is varied, and usually off-the-wall. El Vez with his Hispanic impressions of Elvis Presley remains one of my personal favorites. This year the band was Stoneground. Stoneground was a seminal sixties Bay Area band that split up into Pablo Cruise and the Beau Brummels. This year, twenty-two years after that break-up, they decided to get back together.

Stoneground was terrific. They were high energy with delirious guitar solos, a driving infectious beat, and throbbing vocals. The crowd was into it, big-time, dancing up huge dust clouds as they boogied on the dirt floor. Alas, there were evidently some problems amongst the band members. Chuy told me that he received word that Stoneground was breaking up after his gig. I told Chuy that his concert would come to be known "the Farewell Reunion Tour."

There is never any publicity for Chuy's event. It is strictly word of mouth. Chuy sells 100 tickets, and then tells everyone he is sold out. He prices the event so he just breaks even, and he offers a remarkable dinner buffet on the order of The Last Supper for the price of a "super sized" meal at a fast food chain. Guests are encouraged to bring their own wines, and of course there is no corkage fee.

The variety of wines is what fascinated Jake Lorenzo, that and the sheer number of bottles consumed. There were $100 bottles of Napa Valley Cabernet, $200 bottles of French Burgundy and priceless jeroboams of French Champagne. These wines were passed around for sharing right alongside $12 Monastrells from Spain, $10 Pinot Grigios from Italy, and $8 Malbecs from Argentina. There were homemade Chardonnays, Pinot Noirs, Zinfandels and even Tempranillos. Australian Shiraz, French Rhone and Mendocino Syrah blackened teeth and turned tongues blue.

Wine has always lived a strange dichotomy. While it is one of the most international of products emanating from virtually every continent all over the world, wine is also deeply provincial and localized, with roots deep in individual communities right down to the most specific hillside. What is French food and culture without Bordeaux, Burgundy and Alsace? Imagine Italy without Chianti.

Each winemaking region has its own traditions and tastes. Winemakers work so hard to achieve what they can with what they have, that they never have a chance to pick their heads up and see what is happening around them.

Unfortunately, over time this focus on the local can turn sour. For many years Bordeaux makers fawned over hard, tannic wines with a hit of brettanamyces as the perfect expression of terroir. In the eighties and nineties California winemakers acidulated their wines so that even now they have yet to yield to the gentle roundness of age.

Nowadays, winemakers who are not internationally aware are at a distinct disadvantage. You need to keep current on vineyard practices, not just at home, but all over the world. Some technique developed in Argentina may be just the thing to elevate your vineyard in Mendocino. Some grape variety beloved in Bulgaria may be the perfect grape for that plot of land in Amador County.

Winemakers need to know about biodynamic farming, clones, rootstocks, and vineyard spacing. They need to be current on trellis systems, irrigation regimens and organic pest control. They need to be savvy about oak barrels, oak products and micro-oxygenation. More than anything winemakers need to taste wines made by their competition, both at home and around the world.

Technology and tradition offer an interesting juxtaposition. Too much tradition and you can be left in the dust as the world's taste passes you by. Too much technology and your wines lose their soul. Winemaking has always been a metaphor for life. Mother Nature throws vagaries of weather, pestilence and whim at farmers the world over. How we deal with the challenges we face is what makes us human. We can shrivel up and moan about our plight, or we can dig in and do the best we can with what we've been dealt.

Just before Chuy's concert I spent a week in New York. A friend took me to Birdland to see Oscar Peterson. Oscar has always been one of the most talented, technically proficient and soulful jazz pianists in history. Now a mature 79 years old, he has to be helped to and from the stage. His left hand is gnarled, the fingers pretty much locked into a claw, the effects of a severe stroke in 1993. He has taught himself an entirely new lexicon by which he can play incorporating his restricted left hand as a gentle club, much in the way of Thelonius Monk.

Jake Lorenzo couldn't bear to watch, but I sat with my eyes closed and listened to this man play. His heart and soul poured from his fingers onto the keys and into our ears. His quartet was there for every nuance, giving musical chuckles at every bit of humor, consoling every sad phrase. Periodically I'd have to peek to prove to myself that Oscar's left hand had not been miraculously restored, because the sounds coming from his piano were divine and inspired. For the duration of the set, the entire room sat quiet in rapt attention to the magic on stage. The final rendition of Satin Doll was so fantastic that even Duke Ellington could be heard leading the applause.

As we approach this 2004 harvest with hopes of a great vintage, Jake Lorenzo says you should get yourself some Oscar Peterson. When the rain rots your Chardonnay or when the heat wave turns your prime Cabernet into raisins, don't crumble to the ground cursing Mother Nature. Put on one of Oscar's CDs; crank up the volume and drink in the nurturing soul of a wonder who has faced every bad hand dealt with grace and courage. Let that music inspire you to do uncommon things, and let's hope that Oscar inspires you make your own beautiful music in the bottle.

Ten or twenty years from now, I want to open that bottle. I want to taste how you overcame the strikes of Mother Nature. I want to be inspired by what you have wrought. If it's good enough, Jake Lorenzo will put on some Oscar Peterson and toast you through the night.

Public Service Announcement

Chuy and I were sitting in the lounge of the new wine bar sharing a delightful Domaine Santa Duc Gigondas. The wine showed classic pepper in the nose, had a lovely berry flavor and that lingering finish that comes from ripe (not overripe) fruit and good acidity. Jake Lorenzo knew that we would suck that bottle dry within the hour. Since we had come from a great birthday lunch that included a lovely David Noyes Tocai Friulano, I started to wonder if we needed a ride home. When I mentioned this to Chuy, he said, "I can almost guarantee that we will not be over the legal limit, but if we get stopped that's not to say some overly aggressive law enforcement officer won't go out of his way to prove otherwise."

Jake Lorenzo tries to be very careful about driving when I've been drinking. It's one of the reasons I am on a first name basis with all of the cabbies in the Valley. If I'm hitting it hard, or if I've been drinking for hours, then driving is clearly out of the question. But what if we've enjoyed a four-hour dinner at a friend's house where six of us have consumed four or five bottles, what then?

For my birthday I asked Chuy for a present. I wanted him to explain everything he knew about drinking and driving. Chuy runs the Burrito Palace and serves some of the best Mexican food on the planet, so people tend to forget that he's one of the most talented defense attorneys around. Not Jake Lorenzo, and I know what attorneys charge. I figured lunch and a couple of bottles of wine would save me a fortune in consulting fees.

Chuy says we've learned a lot about drunk drivers, but that there are still a lot of myths surrounding drinking and driving. He started with the good news. The U.S. has a really low fatality rate in general. There are fewer than one and one half deaths for every one hundred million vehicle miles traveled. Alcohol related fatalities have been descending for decades and since 1982 have fallen from 60 percent of all traffic deaths to 39 percent. In that same period, the proportion of alcohol related deaths has dropped 35 percent while traffic deaths not associated with alcohol have risen 53 percent. Still think that talking on cell phones while you are driving isn't dangerous?

Years of experience have shown that prison sentences don't deter drunk drivers, nor do large fines or increased alcohol taxes. What seems to work best is automatic license revocation. It has proven the most effective way to reduce drunk-driving. On the other hand, most drunk driving fatalities are caused by drivers whose blood alcohol content (BAC) averages .16, double the legal limit. These are usually high-risk, repeat offenders. Getting them off the highways would make our roads infinitely safer. Counseling where possible or prison when necessary seem to be the best ways of dealing with these habitual drunk drivers.

"Unfortunately," says Chuy, "the police don't differentiate between these repeat offenders with high BAC and you or me out celebrating a birthday hovering near the legal limit. People try all sorts of crazy ways to beat getting stopped by the cops if they've had something to drink"

Jake Lorenzo knows all about that. It took me months of practice to learn how to recite the alphabet backwards. If I got into my car after having some wine with dinner, I'd wrap my ankle in an ace bandage and have crutches in the back of the car to help with the field sobriety test in case some cop stopped me.

If you are loaded like the clowns you see on *COPS*, that's one thing. Where borderline legal limit drivers are concerned, field sobriety tests (according to Chuy) are a joke. He cited a study conducted by Clemson University scientists where they showed police officers videotapes of people taking six common field sobriety tests. The officers had to decide which of the people were too drunk to drive legally. The officers selected 46 percent of the people as too drunk to drive. What the cops didn't know was that NONE of the participants had a BAC above .000. Those officers could have flipped a coin and come up with the same results.

Breathalyzers aren't much better. Breath analyzers simply aren't precise. They don't measure actual BAC; that can only be done with a blood test.

Breathalyzers try to measure the alcohol in your breath to *estimate* the actual BAC. Under ideal conditions, which are not likely when the test is conducted on a highway by a law enforcement officer, a BAC reading of .08 could indicate an actual BAC of anywhere between .065 to .095. That leaves too wide a range on which to bet your freedom and standing in the community. Not only that, but the concentration of alcohol in your breath changes from the first to the last part of that breath. The first part of your breath is much lower than the last part. Police know this and will exhort people to "Breathe harder!" Just say no.

Chuy explains that people don't understand the law. All those rights we think we have, because we watch all of those cop shows, don't exist UNTIL we are arrested. If cops stop you and ask for permission to search your car; just say no. Be polite, but say no, because once you give them permission, you've given up your rights.

Chuy suggests you use some version of the following: "If I am not under arrest, I'd like to go freely on my way. If I am under arrest, please tell me. In either case, I would like to refuse consent to any search of my person, my effects, my property or my premises. I wish to remain silent, and have an attorney present during any questioning, lineup or search. I wish to speak to my attorney before I will waive any of my rights."

Jake Lorenzo is not trying to find ways around drunk-driving laws. I am not advocating drinking and driving. I am not giving advice so you can be irresponsible. If you make the miserable decision to have too much to drink and then get behind the wheel of an automobile, then you deserve whatever penalties are coming to you. You'll have to man up, like Charles Barkley did. Do the crime and do the time. But if you drink responsibly, then I don't think you need to have your life ruined by an over-zealous police officer looking to put your butt behind bars because you had a couple of glasses of wine.

Part of drinking responsibly demands that we know as much as possible about alcohol and its effects. A glass of wine, a beer or a cocktail all contain about the same amount of alcohol. Drinking slower, alternating water or soda in between drinks, and eating before, during and after drinking will slow intoxication. Remember Jake's axiom: the solution to pollution is dilution. In general, the more you weigh, the more you can drink before getting intoxicated. Coffee, cold showers and exercise will not sober you up. Only time can sober up a person. Alcohol leaves the body of virtually everyone at a constant rate of about .015 percent of blood alcohol content (BAC) per hour.

To learn exactly how much you can consume and what your BAC is likely to be, check out this website and go to their virtual bar. *http://b4udrink.org/lib/shock /index.html*

Drinking impairs your judgment, so don't ever drive if you, or anyone else thinks that you've had too much to drink. Use designated drivers whenever you can. Taxis are well worth the investment, especially when you consider the expense of dealing with a DUI or the tragic consequences of causing a serious injury or fatality.

If you are looking for comprehensive and reasoned information about alcohol and its effects, then Jake Lorenzo recommends this site. *http://www2.potsdam .edu/hansondj/DrinkingAndDriving.html*

New Orleans: The City That America Forgot

Jacques Soulas, co-owner of Café Degas in New Orleans' City Park area, returned home to 6569 Marshall Foch Street in the Lakeview district. Silty grey mud covered the streets and the lawn. Trees bent over at 90-degree angles or lay uprooted on the ground grasping for a purchase in the humid air. Jacques stared at the fluorescent orange "X" on the door to his house, focusing on the "0" in the quadrant reserved for dead bodies.

Shaken, he approached the house, fit his key into the lock and opened the door. He first noticed the paintings, his paintings, more than 100 of them. Years of work on oil landscapes of a city no longer there. The paintings lay in piles, strewn around the studio, each one covered in mud, canvasses torn and cut, frames split and broken by the churning floodwater.

Stepping into the living room, he found everything topsy-turvy. He faced piles of water-sodden furniture; a couch bloated like a dead body, a broken dining room table like a sunken raft. Sheetrock dangled from the ceiling, chunks fallen to the floor to stick in the mud. The walls were coated with fuzzy brown pods of mold exploding into kaleidoscopic patterns.

He slipped in the muck as he made his way up the stairs to the bedroom where everything was pristine, untouched, just as he had left it. Disoriented, he sank down heavily on the bed. He plucked a framed family photo from the nightstand, staring at his own smiling face, and his wife Angela, and his two children, Adrian and Sebastian. He frantically collected all the photos in the room. He fumbled through the drawers and gathered together some clothes, but then he had to get out. He was overcome with an urge to get out of the house immediately.

He made his way down the stairs, photos and clothes clasped to his body. He charged through the muddy living room and then froze in front of his paintings. Grasping his things in his left arm, he reached out tentatively with his right, picking through the paintings in the hope of salvaging this one of the Sculpture Garden in City Park or that one of Bayou St. John, but it was futile.

Overwhelmed, unable to think clearly, not knowing what to do or where to begin, Jacques walked to his car. He tossed the clothes and the photos onto the back seat, turned the key in the ignition and drove away. He drove away from the house he had just purchased eight months earlier, the house he bought so his kids could attend the best public school in New Orleans. He left behind the three-bedroom, two-and-a-half bath, split-level home with the beautiful swimming pool, now filled with muddy water and coated with an iridescence that Jacques would have recognized as somewhere between Transparent Red Oxide and Thalo Blue.

Three months after Katrina, the streets are still muddy, as are the lawns, but now hedges of life's flotsam stand at the curb. Piles of mattresses, refrigerators, toilets, sheetrock and insulation rise in long rows three feet high. Broken dolls, twisted bicycles, useless toasters and computer screens extend the rows to four feet wide. Moldy clothes, mildewed drapes and broken blinds cap the unsightly piles.

Jacques' house still stands empty, layered with the yellow-brown lines that marked the receding water. On either side of Jacques' house are empty, darkened houses marked with the same water lines and colored with the Day-Glo orange "X" and its message of death and destruction. Every house on the block, and every house the entire length of the street and every house in the neighborhood bears this silent testament.

In fact, if you start driving east through Lakeview, a pretty much mid-to-upper class and predominantly white neighborhood, you'll encounter no one, save for the odd tow truck driver hooking up an abandoned mud-covered car. You'll see no lights, except for the occasional street lamp casting eerie shadows on the curbside piles. You'll pass no other moving cars, except for the rare insurance adjuster or demolition crew chief checking out a possible job. You'll fly by local favorite restaurants like Tony Angelo's, La Cuisine and the Steak Knife, all dark and foreboding. All marked with the telltale lines, the fluorescent "X"s. There are no open restaurants. No open gas stations. No open bars, clubs, stores, movie theaters or schools.

If you drive long enough, you'll pass through Lakeview into Gentilly, New Orleans' very first suburb built in the 1940s and 1950s. Gentilly was the site of the first shopping center in New Orleans and the first Howard Johnson's when that meant something. Now, busted out windows in house after house bear silent witness where Natal's nightclub used to pound with music and clinking ice cubes and whispered promises. Where the famous McKenzie's Bakery got its start, upended trees lay like fallen soldiers on a battleground. What was the still lovely, mixed, working-class neighborhood of Gentilly is now empty, deserted, covered in mud and carrying a lingering stench of rotten seafood, putrid chicken and decaying beef.

If you hop up onto the I-10 as the locals call it, you enter New Orleans East. First settled by Gentilly residents displaced by the Interstate Highway, New Orleans East is full of apartments, strip malls, fast-food joints and shopping centers. The Sam's alongside the Interstate is gutted, and so is the Target and the Home Depot. In the parking lot, rows of trailers wait to be distributed by FEMA next to the huge white tents where volunteers still give out water and food and clothes.

New Orleans East was a predominantly black neighborhood, but mixed economically. New Orleans Saints players and famous musicians like Aaron Neville lived in the gorgeous giant houses. Lovely neighborhoods with golf courses sprung up to handle the affluent folks leaving the Ninth Ward, and all sorts of working people lived in the inexpensive apartment buildings.

But not now. Now, no one lives in New Orleans East. The Golden Arches have been bent into broken shards. The Sam's sign slammed into a building and lies shattered. Flooded cars covered with mud hang precipitously over the canals. There are no street lights, stop lights or electric lights of any kind. At night, New Orleans East is dark and empty, and the sheer vastness of that darkness is frightening.

Slipping over to Highway 11 that crosses Lake Ponchartrain, you come to Slidell, once a simple fishing community in St. Tammany Parish. The extraordinary jazz duo, Kim Prevost and her husband Bill Solley, live in Slidell. They purchased their house at 1706 Dunkirk St. in the new King's Point subdivision because housing in Slidell was cheaper than in New Orleans and they thought the environment would be better for their daughter, Sofia.

Slidell is 33 miles due east of Jacques Soulas's house, 33 miles of complete devastation. When Bill and Kim made the long drive from Houston, they knew they would find storm damage, but they hoped that water had not invaded their home. Nearing their subdivision, they saw hundreds of large pines lying on the ground, their trunks snapped like matchsticks. Telephone poles had tumbled, taking power with them. Lower Slidell left them speechless. It looked like a huge bomb had gone off, blowing houses off their foundations, ripping walls off buildings so they looked like doll houses waiting to be furnished. Fishing camps along the lake were completely wiped out, leaving only row after row of dock pilings as a marker.

As they turned onto their block the destruction continued. Trees that had crushed cars and slammed into houses were now strewn about. The water was long gone, leaving mud and dead grass and the piles of personal possessions dragged from the homes. The landscape seemed washed of color and life until it was a faded black and white memory, only it wasn't a memory. It was real.

From the outside, their home looked intact and their dwindling hopes were rekindled. The orange "X" left by the search and rescue teams on their garage door unnerved them. Bill took out his key and went through the front door, while Kim made her way through the snapped trees and the muddy yard toward the bashed in back door.

Bill's first thought upon entering the house was to just shut the door and leave. The floor was slick with mud, the walls covered with black blotches of mold and permeated by that smell. That smell of rotting food, the smell that seeped into your brain and fouled everything you tried to eat for the next week. Sodden furniture sat throughout the house as if left by maniacal movers. The refrigerator stood open in the living room, the couch rested in the kitchen, the dining table squeezed into a bathroom.

Meanwhile Kim stood in the kitchen staring at the mud lines five feet high around her walls. Mud was everywhere; covering Sofia's toys, covering the toy stove where she had spent night after night playing with her daughter pretending to make red beans and rice, and chicken-andouille gumbo, and black-eyed peas, and that's when she lost it and began to cry. She cried because she realized those particular special moments would never occur again. She cried at the mud in Sofia's broken crib, the one that Kim's mother had purchased. She cried for the destroyed recording studio, for the microphones, the pre-amps, the wrecked Rolling 1880 Digital Recording System she and Bill used to record their scintillating jazz music.

Then she heard Bill cry out. She went into the bedroom, and there on the bed were Bill's guitars: all five of them in perfect condition, just as he had left them. No mud, no water damage, no breakage. They held each other. They collected what they could salvage, and they loaded it into the car. Then they prayed and headed back to Houston.

They headed back to their daughter Sofia and the rest of Kim's family, all of whom had been born and raised in New Orleans. They went back to her sisters Tracie and Nikki, her brother Ed, her brother-in-law Jamel, her 94-year-old grandmother Miss Dora, her mother Lorraine and her father, Reverend Edmond Prevost, founder and minister of the First Thessolonian Baptist Church at 840 Caffin Street in New Orleans' Ninth Ward.

If you left Slidell and returned to New Orleans on the Twin Spans of Interstate 10 (except that only one of the Twin Spans remained) you'd pass back through the desolate New Orleans East. Then head left toward the river for 31 miles of misery and darkened houses, and you'd get to what's left of Reverend Prevost's church. The First Thessolonian Baptist Church was one of many churches in the neighborhood, and had served the community for 26 years. Kim remembers the fundraising dinners of her childhood, where the church ladies would fry fish or fry chicken and charge nominal sums to raise money for the less fortunate members of the church. No more. There's no church. There's no minister. There are no church ladies. If there's any chicken, it's rotting in some abandoned refrigerator. If there's any fish, it's drying up in the cracked mud that covers the streets and the lawns and the living rooms of the remaining houses.

The Ninth Ward was a tight-knit community, full of people who had lived their entire lives in New Orleans. Seventy percent of the residents owned their own homes. Mostly black, this was the real heart and soul of New Orleans. Now those homes are empty. All of them are empty. They are empty except for the flies. Tiny, humpbacked coffin flies are all over the place, thousands of them, millions of them. They are most active after butyric fermentation has begun and when corpses are starting to dry. Coffin flies can dig their way through cracks in the soil to get to buried coffins. In the Ninth Ward, they needn't bother. Some of the bodies are still lying out in the open, three months after Katrina.

New Orleans: The City That America Forgot

If you head down Caffin Street and turn left onto St. Claude, go over the Industrial Canal that breached and caused so much of the flooding, and turn left to 1038 Pauline St, you'll be at Charmaine Neville's house in the Bywater district. It's 1.6 miles as a coffin fly flies. Charmaine chose to stay in New Orleans during the hurricane, and at the time of the mandatory evacuation she was caring for a neighbor and couldn't get out. She spent days without food or water, stayed on the roof of a nearby school, was raped by looting gangs, and finally commandeered a city bus and made her way towards Baton Rouge with 23 of her neighbors. Charmaine is a hero, and a musician, and a native of New Orleans.

Charmaine compared her return home to an old black and white Vincent Price horror film. The view from the 610 freeway was sheer desolation. There were no trees, no grass, nothing green. Just mud and emptiness. There were no sounds. No birds, no dogs, no cats, just the dying beeps of smoke detectors.

She came around a corner and saw that her house was still standing. She wept. Mud and gunk were everywhere and bugs and dead fish and the damn flies. Inside, her house was coated with gooey mud. White fuzzy mold grew up the walls, purple dry mold climbed the ceiling and green slimy mold dotted the curtains. Upstairs, where the windows had blown out, everything was wet. The ceiling was caving in, the walls were damp and moldy, and the furniture ruined, but at least there was no mud. There was a tree in her laundry room. Her fence was gone, but there was no mud upstairs.

Charmaine mourned for her Bywater neighborhood, for the two nearby public schools, for the seven churches within five blocks, for the small grocery markets that seemed to be on every corner. She missed her totally mixed neighborhood with its mansions along the river and its simple houses, and even the stark poverty across St. Claude Avenue. She yearned for her neighborhood of rich and poor, black and white, Asian and Hispanic, the neighborhood that was New Orleans.

Charmaine left her house that day, the house in which she had lived for 21 years, and went on the road. She sang in Portland, Oregon, in Washington, D.C., in Atlanta, Georgia, and wherever she sang she told the people in her audience, the New Orleans people, that they had to return home. They had to rebuild their city.

She's back in New Orleans now, where she plans to fix her house and then fix her neighborhood. "We need to have the young people back. We need them to continue the culture; otherwise we'll lose this wonderful, special culture to others. Those other people will rewrite history and claim it for themselves and in doing so they will ruin it."

She wants to help get people back, but they are angry. "I tell them not to be angry with New Orleans," she says. "They can be angry with the President, or the Mayor or the National Guard, because they are the ones who let us down. They're the ones who refuse to help, but not New Orleans. New Orleans didn't do this to us."

Charmaine struggles to be positive. "Chicago came back after the fire. San Francisco came back after the earthquake. I've got faith in God, and I've got faith in the people of New Orleans. If the government won't help us, then we'll have to do it ourselves, but the point is, New Orleans will be back."

Charmaine Neville is her own force of nature and she says New Orleans will be back, but is she as strong as Katrina? When you look at the enormity of destruction, when you consider the vastness of the devastation, when you realize that 25 square miles of close-packed houses, schools, businesses, fast-food shops and shopping centers have been completely destroyed, it's difficult to maintain a positive attitude.

At least 70 percent of the city of New Orleans has been destroyed. 1,300 are dead. 350,000 abandoned automobiles filled with mud are slowly being towed to storage yards. 300,000 inhabitants (and if you count the entire Gulf Coast, a staggering 1.3 million) have been displaced to be scattered around to places like Denver and Salt Lake City and Chicago, where it snows, for God's sake.

The city of New Orleans is essential to the health of Louisiana and the entire Gulf Coast. The city's destruction has affected everyone throughout the state of Louisiana. 40 percent of Louisianans had a friend or family member staying in their homes after the storm. 40 percent said they suffered property damage and lost money because they were unable to work. 31 percent of all Louisiana residents lost jobs or were laid off because of the storms. 11 percent lost their businesses. 39 percent feel anger. 53 percent are experiencing psychological depression, and who can blame them.

For the people who have returned, those who still have houses, or whose houses are somewhat inhabitable, there's the guilt. They live with the guilt that they have survived where others have not, that they have jobs when others don't, that they got a new refrigerator when others couldn't. They spend their days waiting for insurance adjusters, learning the limits of their flood insurance and the particulars of their homeowner's insurance and the minutiae of their contents insurance.

They wait to move into FEMA trailers so they can rebuild their ravaged homes. They wait for crews to put the temporary blue roofs on their damaged houses. They wait for building materials. They wait days for mail. They wait in long lines to replace their driver's licenses. They wait for food at the restaurants and they wait on streets choked with traffic, because survivors are all jammed into the remaining Parishes.

All the local news is about the hurricane. Here's who's coming back. Here's who's not. These restaurants are opening. These are closing. Here's the story of the slow return of inhabitants to mid-City. Here are the heart-breaking pictures of people returning to the Ninth Ward for the first time and confronting their loss, finally, three months after the fact. Every single man, woman and child in New Orleans has lived it, and their hearts break all over again. Every one of them has had to drive down the street, not knowing what they would find. Every one of them has had to confront damage, destruction and loss. Every one of them has had to decide whether to stay or to go.

And through it all, through all of the destruction, devastation and despair, there is the unique wry, sarcastic humor. The ability remains to look at life's tragedies and turn them into something positive. These are the people who stare death in the eye and come out dancing. So, everywhere you look you see things like FEMA trailers decorated with Christmas lights. Christmas trees decorated with rubber gloves, bleach bottles, bits of insulation and insurance papers. The Christmas crèche at the newly reopened Lakeside Mall featured houses with blue roofs and rescue helicopters pulling people from the homes. For people forced to live in second-story homes filled with flood water below, they've created a new lifestyle called "Upstairs Living." At Ralph's on the Park you can order a FEMA Cocktail: "Order it now and we'll get back to you in two weeks."

The people who have returned to New Orleans are desperate to see it come back. Reopen a restaurant and they will come to eat. Reopen a neighborhood bar and they will come to drink. Reopen a club and they will come to dance. Get Mardi Gras on the calendar and they will parade. It's who they are. It's what they do, and they're not changing for any damn hurricane. Hell, in New Orleans, a hurricane is just another drink.

They go back to work. They send their kids back to school. They file reports with insurance companies and argue with the adjusters. They spend every free moment repairing their roofs, hanging drywall in their homes, and replacing broken fences and storage sheds. They try to get back to a normal life. But then they drive into Orleans Parish. They see the water lines on the deserted houses. They see the fluorescent crosses on the doors. They stare at the missing windows, the drowned cars, the broken stoplights, the piles of rubble that once made up the lives of friends and family and neighbors, and they wonder, "Why doesn't the rest of the country know about this?"

There is nothing in the brain that can process the information flooding in through the eyes when you look at what is left in New Orleans. The sheer magnitude of destruction is overwhelming and incomprehensible. Never in modern American history has a major city been so devastated. And people don't know. America doesn't know.

We all saw the dramatic pictures at the Superdome and the Convention Center. All of America held its breath as rescuers plucked people from rooftops. We all saw the bodies and the temporary morgues and the refugee centers. We all wrote checks and donated clothes and time and energy to help. And then we all went on about our lives. We forgot about the people of New Orleans and hoped they'd get the French Quarter up and running in time for Mardi Gras and Jazz Fest.

Those of us with friends in New Orleans call and ask how they are doing. "We're alright," they answer, but they're not. They are guilty and depressed and afraid and in shock. Their city is destroyed and the rest of America doesn't know. The rest of America doesn't care.

Where is CNN now? Who will show the rest of America the devastation? This story may not be as dramatic as Katrina, but it's a much bigger story. This is the story of the life and death of a city, a uniquely American city. It's the story of the life and death of an entire, glorious culture.

This story is not about Jacques Soulas or Kim Prevost and Bill Solley or Charmaine Neville. This story is not about New Orleans or even the Gulf Coast. This story is about America and what it stands for and what it will become. The 1.3 million displaced residents from the Gulf Coast are Americans. They live in the same country we do. What we do to help them will define who we are and what we will become. But America doesn't know.

America had better find out. If New Orleans and her people are left hanging, the road to recovery is a dead end. Every American should go to New Orleans and face the destruction. Consider it a wake-up call. Look at the devastation and soak it all in. Talk to the victims, the politicians and the builders. Then get righteously angry and send in the reporters. Shine the bright light of attention into every dark pile of rubble. Let us all see what the people of New Orleans deal with on a day-to-day basis. Surely, Americans will not abandon their own.

All the insurmountable problems about how to rebuild the levees, how to relieve the anxiety in the black communities, how to foster new businesses are nothing if America decides to fix them. When Americans worked together, we went to the moon. If America wants to, we can build the finest levees the world has ever seen. Americans unlocked the secrets of DNA. If America wants to, we can restore the wetlands and barrier islands that would serve to protect New Orleans from the next hurricane. America designed computer chips and invented the Internet. If America wants to we can completely rebuild and refurbish the homes and neighborhoods of our brethren in New Orleans. America is the birthplace of democracy. Let's use real democratic principles to help local communities participate in their own rebirth. Let's welcome raucous partisan debate, listen to all sides and settle upon a compromise with which we all can live. That's what America is all about.

Right now, New Orleans has died. The funeral procession is long, dark and mournful. America needs to step up, lift the handkerchief of mercy, blow the horn of plenty and second-line its way back to a vibrant, joy filled resurrection. Do that, and America will show the rest of the world what we can achieve. Do that, and we can once again take pride in who we are. Do that, and New Orleans will be reborn even better than it was. Do that, and we'll all want to be in that number.

Preparedness

"What it boils down to is two pair of underwear and a really big bottle of gin," Catherine told me. "When the shit hits the fan, that's all you need so long as you have your life and your family is safe."

The Queen of the Gulf Coast Toonknockers was holed up in a motel just outside of Atlanta a few days after Hurricane Katrina. (Toonknockers is the name we use for a group of about 45 families from New Orleans and the Wine Country, who have been hosting each other to special events for the past 12 years.) Over the next few days Jake Lorenzo's house became the official switchboard for Toons looking for loved ones. They were spread out from Panama City, Florida to Houston, Texas. None of their cell phones worked, so they'd call us, get their temporary land-line numbers and communicate with each other that way.

Jakelyn's mother was like a field general. She'd take notes, write down phone numbers and call everyone with phone numbers and updates. Each night, she'd have a sympathetic gin and commiserate with Catherine as they compared notes and brought each other up to date. After an extended two to three week nomadic journey, most of our New Orleans friends made their way back home.

Just in time for Hurricane Rita.

The attitude was, "We get two hurricanes for the price of one. To hell with it. We're staying." Groups of Toons congregated at undamaged houses, cooked up red beans and rice and drank up their wine cellars. They figured after two weeks of sitting in homes without air-conditioning, there was no sense in saving the wine. "We did like you told us, Jake," they said, "In case of emergency, start with the oldest vintage first."

That was a rough couple of days, especially for Jakelyn's mom. It was hard to stay connected with our friends, and we were terrified that their decision to stay would put them in jeopardy. Since she couldn't get them on the phone, Jakelyn's mother sort of panicked. It was the tuna fish that tipped me off.

Jakelyn's mom came into the house carrying a bag that had 24 cans of tuna fish and a dozen batteries. "There are five cases of bottled water in the car," she told me. "Put two in the garage, two in the wine cellar and one under the house."

I mixed her a quick gin, sat her down and asked, "What are you doing, hon?"

"Preparedness," she answered. "We need to be prepared in case there's an earthquake. Where's the flashlight, I've got to check the batteries."

Jake Lorenzo snuck into his office and called his daughter. I had her call her mother, which calmed her down a bit. That night we heard from our friends in New Orleans with the good news that Rita had missed them, and they were alright.

Still, Jakelyn's mother insisted we get our preparedness kit set up. "We can't do anything about Mother Nature, but we should at least be prepared for an emergency." If I've learned one thing being a detective, it's that you should never argue with Jakelyn's mother. When she gets going on something, no amount of logic or reasoning is going to help. Besides, she had a point. It made sense to have some essential items on hand to help you though an emergency.

We worked out land-line emergency numbers to use in case cell phones went down. We set up meeting places in case we were separated. We stocked up on water, batteries, flashlights and got a portable radio. We made sure we had a couple of pans, some utensils, a can opener, a corkscrew and that the propane tanks were kept full. Basically, we did the regular stuff, but when it came to provisions, I had to get tough. "I'll handle the provisions," I told her. "Man does not live on tuna fish alone."

I went to the Burrito Palace, and told Chuy what I was about. He really got into it. He closed the restaurant, jumped into my car and said, "Let's go, I don't want nobody thinking Chuy Palacios ain't prepared." Chuy took me to restaurant supply places, specialty stores and ethnic markets Here's what we came up with:

Preparedness

The Burrito Palace Emergency Preparedness Basic Provisions Kit
2 pair of underwear
1 1.75 liter bottle of Bombay Sapphire Gin
1 jar of jalapeno stuffed olives (they're great with the gin)
1 liter Centinela Reposado Tequila (man does not live on gin alone)
1 bag red beans
1 bag pinto beans
1 bag rice
1 bag flour
1 bag masa (so we can make tortillas if we have to)
1 container rendered duck fat (to help with the tortillas and to make roux)
1 liter good olive oil
1 liter good vinegar
1 large can escargot (easy to cook, a touch of haute cuisine)
4 cans lump crab meat (for crab cakes and gumbo)
4 cans tuna fish (because Jakelyn's mom already bought so many)
2 cans chipotle peppers (for flavoring just about anything)
5 bulbs garlic
1 bag dried shitake mushrooms
2 cans coconut milk
1 tube anchovy paste
4 cans chicken stock
1 can Tony Chachere's Creole seasoning
1 bottle Sriracha hot Chili Sauce
Salt, Pepper and some basic spices

Chuy and I figured these basic provisions would allow us a simple but varied menu. Depending on what else we could scrounge, we could go from Mexican frijoles to red beans and rice. We could do paella or jambalaya. We could make tortillas or tamales one day and then make a coconut infused curry the next. Then, because the contents of our freezers will need to be cooked (assuming we still have freezers) we need spices to mess around with. When it comes to the wine, hopefully we can reach our cellars, or find the map that reminds us where we've buried our hidden caches. Otherwise, it may mean we become looters. A man's got to do what he's got to do.

As soon as our friends from New Orleans returned home, they got together and they started cooking and drinking. It's what they do, and it's why we love them and New Orleans in general. We have always felt this connection to the Big Easy and her people. It is a connection we've shared for over twenty years.

Captain Jon and I are planning on making a trip to New Orleans in early December. We're going to help them repair their homes. (Remember Jake Lorenzo built his own house not so long ago.) We can help give them shelter for their bodies, but Jake Lorenzo thinks it's even more important to give sustenance for the soul.

Our friends in New Orleans will shortly be out of wine. That which wasn't destroyed outright or soaked in toxic floodwaters was compromised by weeks of hot, humid weather without the benefit of air-conditioning. Jake Lorenzo has organized a mission of mercy and good cheer. With the generous help of Debbie Bell and her DSB/Cobalt trucking company, we plan to collect and ship pallets of wine to be distributed among our friends in New Orleans. We are working directly with 45 families. One third of them work in the wine business as supervisors, sales people, buyers for restaurants, etc.

I am asking each winery to donate *just one case* of good wine to the cause. It's not much and it will do a world of good. True, this won't bring the city of New Orleans back to its feet. It won't address the needs of tens of thousands of newly homeless, nor will it help revive the tourist industry. But it will dramatically raise the spirits of 45 families, all of whom are New Orleans natives. All of whom live and work and entertain in the Big Easy. These are the people that make New Orleans the special place that it is.

Please, cough up just one case of good wine. Don't procrastinate. Do it now. Contact Jake Lorenzo at *jake@winepatrol.com*, or call Jake at (707) 996-5980.

Artman

Jake Lorenzo pushed into Chuy's Burrito Palace tripped over a customer's outstretched leg, fell into the table and knocked over a bowl of the Burrito Palace's justifiably famous hot sauce. "Sorry," mumbled Jake as he righted himself and moved towards the counter, where he sat on the lap of a pretty twenty-something just as she was biting into a Burrito Palace super taco. The young girl squealed in some fear, and a brute of a guy with no neck and a few volcanic pimples leapt to his feet and shouted, "What the hell do you think you're doing?"

Chuy appeared just then, assuaged the young lion defending his girl and guided Jake gently by the elbow to his stool. "Jake, my amigo, how much longer are you going to keep this up?" asked Chuy. "You look like hell. You got scabs and cuts on your shins. Your elbows are scraped, and if you keep bumping into people, pretty soon someone is going to pummel you into detective dust."

Jake sat on his stool, "la silla de Jake," felt blindly for his silverware, clumsily unfolded his napkin and said, "I'd like to start with the Palace chilaquiles topped with an egg and smothered in green chile, and I'd like a cold Bohemia please."

Chuy sighed in exasperation, shook his head and headed toward the kitchen. Then he turned and shouted, "And you look like a *pendejo* walking around in that blindfold."

Jake Lorenzo was in the middle of an experiment. For three days he had lived blindfolded. "I'm experiencing blindness," he explained to Jakelyn's mother and to Chuy and to anyone who asked. His shins were bruised from bumping into furniture. His clothes were stained from spilled drinks. His beard was speckled with food that had dripped unnoticed from forks.

Unbeknownst to Jake, various friends followed him whenever he went outside where they desperately tried to stop traffic as he crossed the busy highway. They'd pick up the spilled apples and produce when Jake shopped. They'd retrieve his change when he paid an $8.00 tab with a hundred and forgot the change. At the shooting range, they'd just point him in the right direction and get the hell out of there. Friendship wasn't worth dying over.

"It all has to do with generosity," explained Jakelyn's mom. "When Jake heard that Eric couldn't get back to his home after Katrina, he tracked him down, got him a ticket and brought him to Sonoma to live with us." The Eric she mentioned was Eric "Artman" Hartman a sight-impaired artist. Eric suffers from a rare eye disease known as Choroideremia which starts out with night blindness, and depending on the individual, eventually degenerates peripheral vision into complete blindness.

Eric explained his remaining vision this way, "If you take a tube from a roll of paper towels and look through it: that's what I can see. At night, or in the dark, I really can't see anything."

Eric "Artman" Hartman lived in Sonoma for two months. He and Jake were inseparable. Each morning they would get up, have coffee and punch down the wines. They'd drive around the valley looking for beautifully lit vineyard scenes, and when they found them, Eric would photograph them with his digital camera. Then Jake would drop Eric at Captain Jon's warehouse where Eric would paint until early evening. From there it was out on Captain Jon's boat or to Jake's house for an elaborate dinner with friends or over to the Burrito Palace for a Mexican feast.

In two months, Eric finished fourteen paintings. He framed them and showed them at Carlo Cavallo's Meritage Restaurant where they hung from Thanksgiving through the New Year. Carlo's patrons found the paintings "Incredible, delightful and inspiring," But they could never believe that they had been painted by a blind man, unless Eric happened to come bumping along with his cane.

Eric was hosted by Laurel Glen, Random Ridge, Relentless Vineyards, Guerrilla Vino and spent so much time at the Benziger Family Winery that the tour guides would lead their groups over to him to hear his story and explain the ins and outs of punching down.

"I never knew that winemaking was such tough work," explained Eric taking great pride in his grape-stained hands. He groaned each morning at the pain in his abs like a real winemaker after weeks of punching down. Not only were his hands covered in paint, but they were decorated with the nicks, scabs and bruises of winemaking.

"Artman" taught us a whole new way to look at Wine Country. A typical ten-minute drive across town stretched to an hour because we were always looking for that perfect vineyard shot. Artman taught us about light and color and the interplay of shadow. He showed us to look for elements that broke up the unending rows of grapes and lent a perspective. Everyone from Jakelyn's mother to Chuy to Dr. Iggy Calamari spent early mornings and late afternoons looking for scenes for Eric.

Winemakers like Ray Kaufman and Bill Hawley dragged Eric to spectacular mountain vineyards at first light, escorted him through golden vineyards in the afternoon and plunked him on dramatic vistas at sunset. It became a contest to see who could find the most perfect scene for the Artman. Jake doesn't know if it was entirely due to looking through Eric's eyes, but I know there has never before been an autumn in Wine Country this bright, extended or memorable in its rich red, golden hues.

That's why Jake Lorenzo has gone the last three days blindfolded. I figure that if Eric can make me see my beloved Wine Country in a whole new light just from describing what he sees, then there's no telling what will happen if I get a feel for what he feels.

Tomorrow Eric and I are going to New Orleans. It's been 95 days since Eric "Artman" Hartman has been home. He knows that his building was in eight feet of water and was uninhabitable for ten weeks. He also knows that his second floor apartment survived and he has a home to which he can return.

Given that Eric has just spent two months living with Jake Lorenzo and his friends in Wine Country, a certain period of adjustment is to be expected. As Eric explained, "Back home I drank wine. But it wasn't a bottle or two per person each night." Jake figures if Eric has to spend a short period of time in a clinic giving his liver a rest, it might serve as a halfway house back to his normal life.

For as long as Artman has vision I hope he can read this and know that he has taught dozens of us here in Wine Country to appreciate our surroundings in a more profound way. He has shown us that courage is dependent on good humor and perseverance, and he has left behind a body of work that will remind us of this stunning new perspective he has given us as a gift in return for our hospitality.

Jake Lorenzo knows that Eric is not returning to the home or city he left. I also know that if New Orleans is to have a future, it needs the vision of good-hearted people like Eric "Artman" Hartman.

Ego and Delusion

Chuy and I were drinking gin at Tujaque's bar in the French Quarter. "Man, oh man, Jake," sighed Chuy. "I been listening to what you told me, but I had no idea. It's bad, man. It's amazingly bad."

Chuy was shaken, and it was my fault. I had just given him a forty minute tour of the ravaged city. We went through the once tony Lakeview district to Gentilly, through Mid-town and then down to the lower Ninth ward. Block after block of abandoned, gutted buildings, piles of demolition detritus and miles of mud-encrusted cars left sitting in rows under the Interstate lent to a depressing feeling of futility.

Chuy chewed an olive, "It's like being in a bad movie where you wake up and all the people are gone. The houses are still there, but there's no one walking on the streets or in the bars or getting gas. It's spooky, Jake." Jake Lorenzo, private eye, nods. It's spooky alright. Everyone has to take in the reality of New Orleans in their own way. Some people are silenced by the devastation. Chuy can't stop talking.

Chuy and a dozen other friends from California have come to the city for Jazz Fest. I felt obligated to drag them through the neighborhoods and force them to confront the reality and enormity of the disaster. Hanging in the French Quarter, going uptown through the Garden District and partying with locals in the suburbs can trick a visitor into thinking New Orleans is doing alright, but that's just an illusion. The deteriorating neighborhoods of ravaged New Orleans sit like a homeless person in front of a fancy restaurant, and there is a natural tendency to avoid eye contact with the unpleasantness of the situation.

On Saturday they held the primary Mayoral election in New Orleans, where 22 candidates vied for the job of Mayor for America's most destroyed city. That's 22 delusional people thinking that they have the answers, that they can muster the votes and that it would be worth spending tens of thousands of dollars for the chance. For all but the two run-off candidates it was an illusion. All that money didn't buy votes, but I suppose it fed their egos.

Ego and delusion are related. When a person focuses upon himself to the exclusion of those around him, it helps to be delusional, because a firm grasp of reality won't support all the self-directed praise and self-congratulation.

Politicians aren't the only ones suffering this malady. There's plenty of this in the wine business. Ego and delusion, I mean. What are so many of these resplendent, glistening wine temples if not testament to their owner's massive ego? Where does the competition to have the deepest cave, the tallest tanks and the most expensive bottle come from if not ego?

Don't get Jake Lorenzo wrong. I've got nothing against ego. After all, ego has produced tremendous art and architecture. Look at Hearst Castle, for example. Ego can even help a simple wine writer address massive national concerns in his monthly column.

If it wasn't for ego, who would even attempt to get into the wine business? It's a very expensive, extremely competitive world with most of the chips stacked against you. A delusional view of opportunity is necessary if you are to make that initial financial investment to start a winery. Most of the people from the owners to the bankers to the winemakers need to feed their egos and share the delusions if they plan on selling $100 bottles of wine and receiving scores of 95 from the likes of Robert Parker and the *Wine Spectator.*

Since we're talking about ego, and Jake Lorenzo has one to be sure, and since I'm in New Orleans for Jazz Fest, I feel the need to offer a suggestion. The devastation of this city and the entire Gulf Coast area is so widespread that the reality of the situation cannot be explained through news stories or television reports. When viewing this disaster, the brain cannot even translate the information it receives through your eyes. Every American needs to come here and see this, and it would help if we did something once we got here.

The wine business could help New Orleans and the Gulf Coast. Make this city and area a prime target in your marketing for the next few years. Come here and work the market, which is surprisingly strong. Spend money in the hotels, restaurants and clubs while you entertain clients and show them your wines. Get to know the buyers and sales reps and the city. Learn about the incredibly rich cultural diversity that makes New Orleans unique in all of America.

Get so many winemakers working the streets of New Orleans that they keep bumping into each other. Have them waiting in line to see restaurant wine buyers. Have them pounding on tables in nightclubs while they buy round after round for their customers. Set up hundreds of winemaker dinners in every restaurant in every neighborhood. In fact, in New Orleans people drink enough for you to set up winemaker brunches. Keep setting up dinners and brunches and lunches until every New Orleanian starts to grasp what we are attempting. Have winemakers beating the bushes, calling on stores, dealing with restaurants until New Orleanians start comparing them to nutria, the ubiquitous water rat in every canal and waterway.

Years from now, "winemakers" would simply be thought of as another subset culture contributing to the Big Easy influence, just like the Africans or the Italians or the Irish. Historians would acknowledge this point in time as a key to the recovery of a great city. They would take note of how winemakers instilled a wine-drinking culture into the greatest party city in the world. They will marvel that selfless winemakers contributing to the rebirth of New Orleans inadvertently devised the model whereby every city in America embraced wine culture.

It's a dream to be sure. This is one private eye that knows better than to depend on the generosity of egotists. Winemakers will ask, "What's in it for us?" Come to New Orleans. Help them recover and you will be rewarded with access: access to the richest musical heritage on the continent, access to a whole world of exciting food and most importantly access to some of the warmest, most cordial people on the planet.

In the face of destruction on the level of that wrought by Hurricanes Katrina and Rita, there is a tendency to just shake your head and give up. Jake Lorenzo says, "Do something. Spend money. Come see for yourself and do what you can."

When New Orleans recovers, it will have happened because one person at a time did what they could. Be one of those people and New Orleanians will embrace you and your wines. Be one of those people and New Orleanians will invite you into their lives. What could be better than that, cher?

The Toonknocker Marketing Plan

Jake Lorenzo is lucky to be alive. I have just survived a 17-day visit from the Gulf Coast Toons. Any Toon visit is a test of stamina, but add the complexities of this compacted harvest and you have a veritable marathon of activity that made me satisfied just to cross the finish line.

For those of you who don't know, Toon is short for Toonknockers. I can't explain what a Toonknocker is, but I would know if you were one. You know you're a Toon if your favorite dance hall is the center aisle of a bus, and your entire travel wardrobe has a one-way ticket. You know you're a Toon if you ask for and follow directions from a blind man, or if you come for brunch and stay for dinner.

Quite simply, the whole Toonknocker experience developed out of a relationship Jakelyn's mother and I formed with a couple from New Orleans. We met Jerry and Catherine Henry almost 20 years ago. Delightful people, we formed a fast friendship. We shared a love for food, wine, good friends and offbeat social gatherings. We enjoyed music, laughter and travel. They introduced us to the wonders of New Orleans, Louisiana and the Gulf Coast. We showed them the splendor of Wine Country, Lake Tahoe and the Mendocino Coast.

Pretty soon we were spending a lot of time together. Jerry was a supervisor for a wine distributor. Jake Lorenzo was brokering California wines in New Orleans. It was a match made in heaven. We'd work together all day driving through the city, visiting accounts, and building friendships. Miss Catherine and Jakelyn's mom pitched in and we created the Waitstaff Ball, where we threw an annual party for all of the waitrons in the city. It was a gigantic success and the four of us remain welcome, honored guests in any restaurant in New Orleans.

Jakelyn really liked them, and before we knew it, she had moved to New Orleans to finish her college education. We loved the idea. We knew she had someone there to help her, and it gave us more excuses to visit. We spent so much time in New Orleans that people thought we lived there. Even Jerry and Miss Catherine's kids thought we were relatives.

The hardest thing to do in a relationship is to find another couple to hang with. That rare situation where all four people get along makes for devoted friendships. When you find such a friendship, you must dedicate yourself to it. For the past 20 years we have spent four to six weeks every year with them in New Orleans. They visit us here in Wine Country two to four weeks each year. We have traveled together to France, Spain, and Italy. We have explored Mexico, Nicaragua, Costa Rica and Chile. We have enjoyed the charms of American cities like New York, Chicago, Denver, Santa Fe, and Seattle. Jakelyn's mother and I would rather spend time with Jerry and Miss Catherine than just about anyone outside of our immediate family.

In the beginnings of our relationship, we'd visit them in New Orleans. We'd be out most nights for cocktails, food and late night music. At least once during each visit, we'd arrive back to their house in a highly inebriated state and Jerry would say, "Have you guys ever heard of Arthur Prysock?"

"Sure," I'd reply, "I love his singing voice. What ever happened to him."

"I'm not sure," Jerry would answer. "I guess he died."

We'd spend the next few hours sipping cognac, listening to old Arthur Prysock records on his turntable. To this day Jake Lorenzo still associates Arthur Prysock with early morning headaches.

One day, I was checking out the daily Jazz Fest schedule. Right there in black and white, it said that Red Prysock was playing in the Jazz Tent with his bother Arthur. I ran over to the kitchen where Jerry was waiting for the coffee to perk. "Check this out. We thought he was dead."

"Well," he replied, "if we thought they were dead and they come to town, we've got to go see them."

That became the first Toon rule. We saw some really good acts that way. Of course, we're going back a long time, so several of those acts we thought were dead, actually are. It doesn't matter, if they come to town, we're still going to see them.

After a few years, it occurred to the four of us that it was selfish of us not to share this wonderful camaraderie we had developed. That's when we started Toonknockers. We decided to hold an annual event, invite carefully selected guests, and slowly build a group of people who enjoyed each other's company and would pitch in to create events that would entertain us.

We tied the event to French Quarter Fest, a typical New Orleans festival held in the French Quarter featuring a dozen stages, hundreds of musical acts, and food from all of the finest restaurants in New Orleans. Jakelyn's mom and I would invite a dozen guests, and we would arrive for a four-day party. The first night might be a cruise on the river, or a simple meal in a local joint followed by a night at Rock 'n' Bowl. One night is a full-blown multi-course wine dinner at a first-rate restaurant like Bella Luna, Café Giovanni or Dakota. One night is always dedicated to a crawfish boil where the entire mishpucha, kids and all attend. Sunday we'll rent hot tubs at the local Baseball Park and watch a game, or go to some early evening cabaret. Somewhere in there is the bus ride, which is impossible to describe to anyone who has not experienced it, and a visit to the drive-through daiquiri stands.

We've now been holding this event for eleven consecutive years. We alternate between New Orleans and Wine Country. One year we make the trip out there and they host us. The next year, they come out here and we host them. We're very restrictive about who we invite to the event and have managed to keep it relatively small. We usually have five to six specific events during a Toonknocker weekend with 30-60 people attending each one. Over the course of the weekend, we will consume an average of 25 cases of wine.

Toonknockers could save the wine industry. Imagine if every community had a group like Toonknockers and what if they each had an annual event like ours. Not only would they be spreading camaraderie, friendship and fun, they'd be sucking down truckloads of wine.

And you know we don't just drink during the event. We drink during the planning sessions, the work parties, and the test runs. We make excuses for testing recipes, discussing napkin colors and making sure the wine pairings are just right. We taste flights of wine and do vertical tastings until many of us are horizontal. We have introduced dozens of people from Wine Country to the people of New Orleans and Louisiana. They in turn have brought dozens of people out to California to partake of Wine Country living.

You attend an event where 50 or 60 people are having a wonderful time together, and you anchor that event around good food and fine wine, then those people are going to drink wine often to remind themselves of the event. They are going to return home to their families and friends and talk about the experience. They're going to share that favorite bottle of wine they discovered.

Jake Lorenzo thinks that people in the wine business need to remember how much fun drinking wine can be. Remind yourself. Get a bunch of friends together, plan some sort of event and pop a lot of corks. If you have a good time and you all get along, then invite some other friends and do it again.

The wine you sell may be your own.

He Ain't Heavy, He's My Bottle

"I feel like I've been in a street fight," Chuy moaned, "and I didn't come out on the winning end. Everything hurts. Whenever I move, I find myself groaning like an old man. What happened to me Jake?"

"Toonknockers, compadre. All that happened to you was Toonknockers."

They have all left now, but it was a brutal week. 22 Gulf Coast Toons swept into Sonoma for the 13th annual Toonknocker Patrol. Another 20 Left Coast Toons did the hosting and in the aftermath, my good friend Chuy hurts every time he moves.

Most of the Gulf Coast Toons left New Orleans early in the morning amidst mixed emotions knowing it was their first trip since Hurricane Katrina almost two years ago. They checked into their hotel and immediately flocked to local wineries for some serious wine tasting. That night kicked off with a treacherous expedition up Cavedale Road to the top of Random Ridge high in the Mayacamas Mountains where Bill and Susan Hawley entertained us with their wines, wonderful food and breath-stopping views. The hard-earned spectacular views of Random Ridge are stunning to anyone, but for people who reside in Louisiana where the highest thing in the state is an overpass or a drunken tourist on Bourbon St., the sweeping vistas of the Bay Area and Mount Tamalpais become indelibly etched in the memory banks.

Friday was filled with more wine tasting and an amazing five-course, wine-paired dinner at Deuce, the first recipient of the WinePAL® wine list certificate for fair pricing. Saturday featured lunches at two different Sonoma restaurants, drinking in the park, a giant Louisiana style crab boil in Jakelyn's mom's garden and a night of Zydeco dancing at Little Switzerland. Sunday started with Brandy Milk Punch and Tequila Sunrises, followed by sparkling wine and a delicious brunch before settling into serious wine drinking. From there it was back to our house for Lan's Crab Fat Soup and Crab Meat Maison.

Every evening was filled with late night partying and dancing till the wee hours of the morning. It is the accumulative eating and drinking that wears you down. Jake Lorenzo gained eight pounds in ten days.

Generally, extra weight is a bad thing, especially on aging private eyes. I'll have to spend the next few weeks eating salad after salad in the hopes of returning to my svelte normal body weight. Chuy says that eating salad is, "Greening your diet, and green is in, carnal."

Green is all the rage in the wine business these days. A lot of it makes sense, but as far as this detective is concerned some of this "green" is simply ridiculous. I can hang with certified organic. I respect people who farm without fertilizers, pesticides, herbicides or fungicides. I like the idea of drinking wine less likely to make my nose glow in the dark. I like growers who take the extra effort to care for their vineyards without poisons and figure natural methods for handlings pests and weeds.

Sustainable farming strikes me as "organic lite." There's no real legal status monitoring sustainable farming, but Jake Lorenzo finds it easy to support recycling and conserving water and energy. I like the idea of cover crops and compost and reduced pesticide use. If nothing else, the practice of sustainable farming forces growers to think about the effects their farming practices have on the environment around them, which can't hurt.

Biodynamics is like organic on steroids. Oops, did I say steroids? What I mean is that biodynamic farming is the most intense form of organic farming. Biodynamic farming attracts people who say, "If a little bit is good, then a whole lot must be better." This detective has a hunch that devotees of biodynamic farming are a very competitive lot, the kind of people who will ski the toughest mountain, ride the gnarliest bike trail and chug the most beers.

To tell the truth, Jake Lorenzo likes biodynamic farmers too. I like people who push things to their limits. Burying stuffed cow horns by the light of the moon, working with energy fields of water, creating habitats for creatures and fauna that may help the environment all make some sort of sense to me. If you believe, then Jake Lorenzo says go for it.

I guess what frustrates me is that so many people don't see the big picture. They farm organically or sustainably or biodynamically. They spend weeks trying to find recycled paper and natural inks for their labels. They carefully separate their glass and plastic and cardboard for pickup. They feel good about it and even use their "green" sense to sell their wines to like-minded people.

But there is an inconvenient truth in the wine business. For all the talk about green this and green that, and for all the sustainable farming and recycling and composting, wineries are wreaking havoc on the planet with their oversize bottles. It's bad enough that fat, heavy bottles don't stack in wine racks. These bottles cost more and use more glass. When you ship them, because they are heavier, fewer cases fill a container. Because fewer cases can fit into a container, the cases are more costly to ship, use more gas and end up harming the environment.

Your average full case of wine weighs in at 35 pounds. Truckers figure a full container will hold 22 pallets of wine or 1,232 cases, which makes a full load gross about 80,000 pounds. New premium bottles now weigh between 1,000 and 1,200 grams apiece. These new heavier bottles tip the scales somewhere between 45 and 50 pounds per case. Truckers will max out their maximum gross weight of 80,000 pounds with as few as 880 cases.

That means trucks are shipping 25 to 30 percent fewer cases on each load that is filled with heavy bottles. A 10,000 case winery would go from eight truck loads to eleven. A 100,000 case winery would go from 81 loads to 113. That's a lot of extra fuel to burn, not to mention extra emissions, road wear and driver time.

A loaded semi-truck filled to its 80,000 pound gross weight is lucky to average 6 miles per gallon of fuel. That fuel is costing about $3.00 per gallon. Ship a load from San Francisco to Chicago, which is a distance of 2,132 miles and heavy cases will cost you an extra 90 gallons of fuel. Ship that wine the extra 800 miles to New York and those fancy bottles will use an extra 120 gallons of fuel.

I'd hate to think that the real reason we are fighting in Iraq is to provide enough fuel so wineries can continue to ship their fancy, heavy designer bottles.

I know what you are thinking. You think I've been spending too much time with Michael Moore. It's not true. I'm just a simple detective in Sonoma who is pretty sure that no matter how much cardboard you are recycling, it won't make up for the planetary cost of an extra 120 gallons of fuel.

He Ain't Heavy, He's My Bottle

Want to do something to really help the planet? Use lighter bottles. It won't just help the environment. It will help the truckers, warehouse workers, and bottling line grunts who have to lift those cases. It might even help the garbage men who have to throw the empties away.

A Miracle

It's a miracle, a flat out miracle.

Our dearest friend in New Orleans, Mr. Jerry, was ill. In fact, he was in the hospital and Jake Lorenzo wasn't sure he would get out. Then some tiny, but brilliant doctor from Sri Lanka found the problem. Mr. Jerry was infected with *Pseudomonas aeruginosa,* a particular hardy, insidious bacterium. There is hardly any tissue that Pseudomonas cannot infect if the tissue defenses are compromised in some manner, and Mr. Jerry has some seriously compromised immune issues so he was a perfect target.

The doctor put my friend on a severe antibiotic regimen that involved receiving drip treatments three to four times a day for six to seven weeks. Each day Mr. Jerry was hooked up to a machine for five hours. Each day the wound that had provided the entry point for the infection had to be cleaned and bandaged. Several days each week, he had to go to the hospital where his liver and blood levels were monitored to track how they were handling the medicine. Whenever he met with the Sri Lankan doctor, the doctor would give him a cookie and tell him, "We will beat this infection."

When Jakelyn's mother and I visited Mr. Jerry last January, he was in the fifth week of treatment and was starting to rally. In fact, he had improved enough that we were able to celebrate his birthday at Galatoire's. It was the first time he had been out in months. He walked slowly and had to use a cane, but he made it to the dinner.

Last week, when we returned to New Orleans, Mr. Jerry was much improved. Walking without a cane and freed from the restrictive drip regimen of antibiotics, he was returning to his funny, sarcastic self. We went out to Mr. B's for dinner and then made our way to the Bombay Club to hear Luther Kent.

A Miracle

The walk from Mr. B's to the Bombay Club was four or five blocks. A light rain was falling, but all of a sudden my detective instincts kicked in and I noticed that the French Quarter was hopping. Mr. B's had been packed. There were lines out the door of Acme, Felix's and Deanie's. Bourbon St. was mobbed. Even the Bombay Club was crowded until the last set at midnight. Walking back to our cars at 1 AM, music blared from the open doors, revelers danced in the streets and traffic was bumper to bumper. Jake Lorenzo hadn't seen the French Quarter like this since Hurricane Katrina.

People tend to forget that, for the most part, New Orleans survived Hurricane Katrina in good shape. It was the failure of the levees and the subsequent flooding that caused the major damage. The ruptures of the levees compromised the city's defenses and the toxic flood waters spread throughout the city like a virulent Pseudomonas bacteria. It has been a long, hard road to recovery and there have been setbacks like Hurricanes Rita and Gustav, but from where Jake Lorenzo is sitting, it appears that the medicines are starting to have an effect. New Orleans may be weakened, but it is definitely coming back.

Because Mr. Jerry was feeling better, we slipped back into our normal day to day activity, which centered around eating in great restaurants. There are more restaurants open and operating in New Orleans now than before Katrina, and this is in a city that lost 20 to 25 percent of its population. The food is as good as ever. From grand classics like Galatoire's to Commander's Palace, to favorite neighborhood places like Clancy's and Pascal's Manale to new favorites like Coquette and Lillette the food of New Orleans is fantastic.

It's the wine prices that are stupid.

In most places a glass of wine starts at $8 per glass and quickly escalates to $14, and that's for a *four ounce pour*. You never find wine on a list below $30 per bottle and there is very little worth drinking below $40. Faced with these exorbitant, inflated wine prices this detective opts for cold, frosty pints of local brew or one of the delicious cocktails served at any establishment in the city.

Even banking executives partying in the Crescent City and trying to spend their bailout money bonus checks pause when presented a wine list in New Orleans. Look around the tables in the restaurants and you see everyone is still drinking, but precious few are drinking wine. There are fewer containers waiting to be unloaded at the city's distributors, and that means less truckers are hauling those containers, which is proof that less wine is being ordered.

All those winery accountants with their noses pressed up against the bottom line are pushing alarm buttons. They are shouting, "The sky is falling. The sky is falling." Winery owners are listening, evidenced by a look at the *Wine Business Monthly* listing for grapes and bulk wine which is beginning to take on encyclopedic volume. Turrentine, Ciatti and the other bulk sales entities have so much available bulk wine that they could flood New Orleans anew if they let it slip through the levees of commerce.

This whole wine pricing thing has gotten out of hand. Like a rampaging Pseudomonas infection it is raging through the land and threatening to take out wine life as we know it. Well, Jake Lorenzo is no doctor and I'm certainly not from Sri Lanka, but I think we can beat this infection and I'll give you a cookie.

We don't need any more mediocre $40 bottles of Merlot and Cabernet. $150 bottles of wine smack of greed and snobbism and just don't fly in an Obama world. The poor American wine consumer has been beaten and battered by ridiculous wine pricing for years now. We need to get them on a strict daily regimen of decent wine at fair prices. What if all of those famous winemakers making their expensive bottles of wine took this time to challenge themselves? Get out there on the bulk wine market, find all those hidden treasures, and use your gifted talents to create some truly exciting blends.

Find some new, unique, light-bodied, "green" packaging and get those wines out into the market at prices the public can afford. Load up all those empty containers with low-priced, delicious wines and ship them to our financially strapped friends in places like Fargo, Seattle and Florida. Make the prices so attractive that restaurants can afford to sell a glass for $4. Put them on the wine shelves at $5.99.

We have plenty of winemakers with the ability to make this happen. It's been fun working with the finest grapes and the best equipment to create some of the best wine in the world. Now it's time to roll up your sleeves and get back into the muck. Do some heavy lifting, challenge those old palate muscles and make something special. The bulk wine is out there. The pricing is attractive. The time is now.

A Miracle

Every economic crisis provides an economic opportunity. Jake Lorenzo says that the wine industry should take advantage of this one. Think of it as our industry's private stimulus package. John Q. Public could use a drink, and in these economic hard times old John Q. should have one that he can enjoy.

Really good wine, at a really fair price. Now that would be a miracle, a flat out miracle.

The Olympics

On a quiet Monday morning, Jake Lorenzo saunters through the front door to Chuy's Burrito Palace. He pours a cup of coffee, steps behind the counter, pulls out the bottle of Hornitos and adds a shot to his cup. He sits down on his stool, "la silla de Jake" and wonders where Chuy has gone.

Jake hears a muffled thump and then a groan. He stands and makes his way through the kitchen. An aromatic pot of beans bubbles away on the stove. Piles of chiles, onions, tomatoes and cilantro wait expectantly on the cutting board in anticipation of becoming Burrito Palace salsa. Another muffled thump and then the groan, which Jake now recognizes as Chuy's voice. Jake grabs a large, heavy skillet and silently glides across the kitchen to the back door. He eases up to the open door and peers out into the yard. Jake Lorenzo, private eye, drops the skillet in fear.

Chuy has erected a high bar behind the Burrito Palace. Piles of thick foam rubber are spread all around, looking like an explosion in an upholstery shop. Chuy jumps up and grabs the bar. He pulls himself up and starts to swing in slow giant turns. Gathering speed, Chuy releases from the bar, hurtles over it and makes a desperate grab. He misses, landing heavily on the pile of foam rubber, expelling a loud groan.

As Chuy struggles to his feet, Jake steps through the door. "What's up, carnal?"

Chuy is sweating. "Hey, Jake, it's these damn Olympics. I just can't believe what they do on that high bar."

"Well, you're not exactly looking like one of the Hamm twins on that bar, amigo."

"Yeah," Chuy agrees, "but I've only been working at it for three days. All I want to do is hit one of those release moves. Then I'm done. I mean when you let go, it's like falling out of a building. Catching that bar and having the momentum pull you through another swing has to be awesome. I've got to have me some of that."

"Well, Jake Lorenzo has got to have some chorizo and eggs," I say. "What about taking a break."

Chuy agrees to put his high-flying dreams on hold and sets to making his earthbound magic in the kitchen. As I savor the perfectly spiced dish, I think about how much importance each of us gives to what we are doing at any given moment, and how inevitably we must move on after that moment has passed.

Imagine the training, dedication and talent it must take just to be an Olympic athlete. Years and years of workouts, coaching sessions and continual practice allow athletes to slowly develop their skills. Then each country has trials to qualify for the Olympic games. Dozens of top-flight athletes from all over the world end up qualifying for each event. Once they get to the games, they must endure a series of qualifying heats, semi-finals and then the finals. There's just one gold medal. On that particular day, for one particular moment, some particular person is the best.

Then what?

In the Olympics we see people dedicated to running, jumping, and swimming. We also see people dedicated to rowing, target practice and trampolining. At the winter Olympics, we watch ice-skating, ski racing and ski jumping. We also see ice sweeping where contestants chase that bowling ball thing across the ice with brooms.

It is a very human thing to dedicate oneself to a goal. People dedicate themselves to all sorts of goals. In fact, you might not think all of the goals are worth this dedication. Some of them are just silly. Take jugglers for example. How many hours does it take before you can keep three balls suspended in the air? How long for five balls? What about the guys who can juggle a chain saw, a live fish, and a twinkie while reading comic books on a unicycle? That can't be easy. It requires dedication, but is it justified?

See, the secret to all this training is that the end reward isn't the big deal. It's the process of getting there that matters.

You want to think of a dedication that's silly. How about winemaking? Hell, throw a bunch of grapes into a bucket and they'll turn *themselves* into wine. Still, winemaking is an Olympian type effort. In California alone hundreds of winemakers are competing to find that perfect vineyard. They're agonizing over the optimum picking time, the most advantageous yeast, and the best barrel. They're sweating cold stabilization, heat stabilization, malolactic fermentation and brettanamyces infection.

Once they get their act down and get the wine into the bottle, then they have to compete. California winemakers have to compete with winemakers from Oregon, Washington, New York, Texas, Missouri and dozens of other states. Once they get through those trials, they must face the world. Spain, France and Italy aren't conceding any gold medals. Emerging Eastern bloc countries have reinvigorated programs, and the Aussies are coming on strong.

Winemakers study and practice and learn and relearn. Occasionally, they fall off the high bar. (Well, actually during crush they are more likely to fall asleep *in a bar* after a grueling day on the crush pad.) Competition is fierce, international and worldwide.

I think we put far too much emphasis on winning. It's the process that's important. It's those daily decisions, the continuous challenges, and the will to succeed that teach us to become the people we will turn out to be. I have as much respect for the athlete who struggles to win the state time trials as for an Olympic gold medalist. I can take just as much delight in drinking a bottle of wine from New Zealand as one from California, France or Italy.

Winemakers have something over all the great athletes, because when athletes look back on their accomplishments, when they gaze upon their trophies and medals, they only have fading memories.

When winemakers drink their own wines, we get high. The very stuff we produce reminds us of the excitement of harvest. The heady flavors and aromas of crush live on in the bottle. The intoxicating exhaustion of a 16-hour day can be exactly duplicated with the right amount of imbibing.

Jake Lorenzo knows Chuy Palacios. Chuy will keep working on that high bar. When Chuy finally releases and recaptures that high bar, he's going to be excited. He will be adrenalized, pumped up and as fired up as an habanero pepper. Then he will come over to our house, sit down with us and have some wine. He will regale us with stories about his quest. He will describe the feeling of achieving his goal. If we pace ourselves just right, if we drink the perfect amount of wine, Jakelyn's mom and I will be just high enough to feel our hands catch the high bar after the release, and we'll share Chuy's exhilaration.

Once that happens, we'll have to set another goal. We'll need to test ourselves in another way. That's why Jake Lorenzo has built a petanque court in his backyard. Chuy's spirit may soar, but like his good friend Jake Lorenzo his aging body should not be flying through the air in anything short of an airplane headed for some exotic local. So we'll practice petanque on lazy summer afternoons until after weeks of coaching, months of training and years of practice, we're ready to fly to France and take them on head to head and bottle for bottle.

Zinfandel

Chuy is on a big Zinfandel kick. I have no idea how it started, but for the last month, all he will talk about is Zinfandel. All he will drink is Zinfandel. Jake Lorenzo doesn't see Zinfandel as the best fit for a Hispanic attorney who makes his living slinging pots of beans and blistering salsas, but there's no stopping Chuy when he gets going.

"Jake, Zinfandel is the most Mexicano grape in the world," he insists in his stentorian closing argument voice. "The range of aroma and flavor is extraordinary and it's directly linked to the place where it is growing. Napa Zins have a completely different character than Amador Zins, and they are completely different from Paso Robles Zins."

Jake Lorenzo doesn't like to argue with attorneys, especially Chuy, but I can't help myself. "Mexicano grape. What the hell are you talking about? Zinfandel came from Croatia. Last I checked, not a lot of your people came from there. Are you telling me you like those overripe, over-oaked, high alcohol monsters loaded with residual sugar that taste like a cross between Port and compote?

"Not my style, amigo," shrugs Chuy, "but it's still a style and lots of people like it. I'm trying to explain that Zinfandel may not be Mexicano per se, but it reflects our culture."

Jake Lorenzo can feel himself sinking into the quicksand of attorney debate. Chuy loves esoteric arguments the way private eyes like gorgeous clients with big, liquid eyes, pouty lips and a propensity to pay in cash. "How does Zinfandel reflect Mexicano culture?" I ask, knowing that I've just stepped into some horrible Mel Gibson/Apocolypto trap that could end with him standing over my body figuratively holding my beating heart in his hand, another twisted sacrifice to the gods of debate.

Chuy explains that Mexico is regional, and that each region brings its own style and variation to classic dishes. You can get *carnitas* all over Mexico, but the Jalisco style is much different from the Michoacan style, which is nothing like Yucatecan carnitas. "You see," he persists, "the food reflects a sense of place, just like Zinfandel."

Chuy insists that this sense of place is central to all things Mexicano, at least when it comes to food and drink. He ticks off the use of black beans in the south, pinto beans in the north and white beans on the Yucatan. He rambles on about red pozole versus white pozole, the seven different moles and variations in shrimp cocktails up and down the Pacific coast. He argues that tequila, mezcal, sotol and bacanora are just variations on the same theme influenced by place and custom.

"That's why I say Zinfandel is the most Mexicano grape," he announces. "There's just one thing I want to know, Mr. Hotshot Detective. Why? What is it that gives this one grape such an adaptable, chameleon-like quality? Cabernet has nuances of place, but it's all Cabernet. Pinot Noirs from different regions vary in delicate layers of complexity, but remain at their core Pinot Noir. Only Zinfandel grows to be different animals in different places."

Chuy turns and walks off, leaving me like a puffing bull watching a tight-pantsed matador after he's delivered the death blow. I mean, this detective has to admit that Zinfandel seems to have a limitless variety of styles, flavors and aromas. Zinfandel is so expressive of where it is grown, that it can taste completely different from one region to another. Mountain vineyards taste different than flatland vineyards. West facing vineyards differ from south facing vineyards. There's no mistaking the cherry cola notes of Amador Zin from the earthy character of Paso Robles. There's the bright high-acid style of Mendocino County and the rounder, almost Burgundian character of Napa.

I've had Zinfandels as light and fruity as fresh Beaujolais that were delightful in their youthful exuberance. I've had classic Zinfandels rich with complex berry and plum flavors, others with intense ground black pepper flavors and still others with sumptuous raspberry jam character. Then there are the monsters with their glycerol high alcohol and ripe, Port-like character. Zinfandel can be all things to all people. When they are well made, I like them all.

There's the rub. There's a lot that can go wrong with Zinfandel. There's something about making good Zinfandel that's more difficult than it looks.

Zinfandel

Zinfandel has thin skins and grows in tight bunches. Put some rain in the picture or a week or two of fog and you've got a mold growing potential that could make your vineyard look like a furry chunk of brie that's been hiding in the corner of your refrigerator for six months.

When you look at a bunch of Zinfandel grapes you'll observe some grapes that are raisining, others that seem perfectly ripe and still others just starting to color. This uneven ripening of Zinfandel makes for unique fermentation dilemmas. Throw those grapes into a tank and they'll test 24° Brix, but the next day they'll be at least 26° Brix. If the grapes are low acid, you've got to watch for VA. Higher sugars make the wine susceptible to lactobacillus. Inattention and high alcohol can lead to aldehydes. The alcohol makes the yeasts weak and less likely to finish fermentation, which leads to sweet, high-alcohol red wines. Then there's the oak. All that alcohol can extract a lot of oak flavor, especially if you use too much new oak, which can easily mask the more delicate aromatic charms of the variety.

People think that a wine with all that muscular alcohol is tough and can be bounced around, but it turns out that fine Zinfandel exists in a delicate balance between power and finesse. Disrupt that balance and the wine has the potential to be dominated by its least attractive elements. If Zinfandel had a personality, it would be bi-polar. It's a wine capable of gorgeous, exhilarating depth and complexity, but it has the potential for depressing, overwrought excess.

Now that I think about it, Chuy is wrong. Zinfandel isn't the most Mexicano grape. It's the most American. Zinfandel can grow most anywhere, although it prefers hot days and cool nights. It follows no rules and insists on a fierce independence. It's up-front and in your face with a likeable desire to please, but if you study it closely, you'll find complex layers of personality just below the flamboyant surface.

Zinfandel makes no excuses for youthful exuberance and shows little reverence for doting tradition. It appreciates attention, but has enough independence to make its own way. It wants to be liked, but insists that you take it for what it is and not something it is not. In the sometimes formalized tradition of wine Zinfandel is fun, informal and a little brash.

That sounds American to me.

Making Waves

It's 104 degrees and Jake Lorenzo is sitting in the hot tub. Chuy Palacios is with him sucking down some ice cold Negro Modelo beers. A few days earlier, when the weather prognosticators convinced him that a genuine heat wave was headed for Sonoma, Jake drained half the tub, filled it with cold water from the hose and then dumped in the contents of his ice maker. The two friends sat lounging in cool 82 degree water.

"You know what Sonoma needs, Chuy?" Jake asks rhetorically. "Sonoma needs a beach. If we had a beach, right here in the neighborhood, I'd never have to visit Mexico again. I'd have it all right here in my back yard."

"Well, Señor Detective, unless some humongous earthquake splits things just right, you ain't got no chance of that beach turning up."

"But look at Highway 12," admonishes Jake. "We've got three Mexican markets in just one block. They sell homemade *chorizo* and *longoniza*. They have pig heads, cow heads, intestines and *nopales*. On weekends they sell *carnitas*, *birria* and *barbacoa*. The burrito wagon comes every night, and has sprouted a Mexicano version of a strip mall with other people vending *tamales*, CDs and DVDs of all the latest movies. Hell, on Thursdays the County sends out a truck that gives free HIV and Hepatitus C blood tests. We might as well be living in Mexico."

"Amigo, I've got to admit that it warms my heart to see all the *gente* walking up and down the highway," agrees Chuy. "I guarantee you that if we built a central plaza and park in Fetters Hot Springs, people would flock to it every night and promenade around it just like in Mexico, especially if you put a church at one end of it."

"I'm telling you Chuy, all we need is the beach," says Jake. "Maybe we can get one of those wave machines like they have in Arizona. We'll build a giant lake right here in Fetters Hot Springs. We can fire up that wave machine and body surf to our heart's content. It would immediately turn into the biggest summer attraction in Wine Country.

Chuy smiles, "I can see the kids walking up and down that sandy beach selling homemade tamales, and jewelry and chile covered mangoes on a stick."

"I can smell the *elotes* roasting in the evening," Jake exclaims, "and since we're in Wine Country you could operate Chuy's Palapa Wine Bar, where you'd serve ice cold beers and thirty wines by the glass, all under $5 per glass."

Clearly the heat of the day curdles the mind, even when you're relaxing in a perfectly cooled tub. Imagine a beach, where you could body surf in the heart of Wine Country. Sounds pretty far-fetched, especially in an area where fifty-year-old shacks sell for $500,000 and vineyard land starts at $70,000 per acre.

Then again, this is Wine Country and all kinds of far-fetched ideas have become reality. Jake Lorenzo thinks there is no such thing as an idea that is too outlandish, as long as you dedicate yourself to fulfilling that idea.

In the 1970s, a few people had an idea. They thought they could take grapes, which weren't selling for a lot of money, and turn them into some decent varietal wines. The far-fetched idea was "varietal wines," because all the public knew was white, red and rosé. People dedicated themselves to this project. As they worked on it, they found it much more complicated than they had imagined. It wasn't enough to pick the grapes and ferment them into wine. The wine had to be aged in barrels, bottled, possibly filtered, and then marketed. The winemakers learned about yeast, malolactic bacteria, heat and cold stabilization, volatile acidity and brettanomyces infection. They educated their customers to appreciate what they had to offer, and over time their far-fetched idea became reality. Varietals ruled the land.

By the time we got to the 1980s varietals were all the rage and the far-fetched idea moved to barrel fermented chardonnays, induced botrytis and softened tannins. Winemakers learned about lees contact, stirring the lees and racking. For a decade people drank lush, buttery Chardonnays and soft, voluptuous Merlots.

The 1990's pushed the envelope. Scientists had created devices that allowed winemakers to create any kind of wine they imagined. Letting the fruit hang until fully ripened at 26 degrees Brix was the far-fetched idea, and unctuous, highly extracted, honey-textured wines brimming with ripe, exotic flavors were the Holy Grail. Micro-oxygenation, reverse osmosis, yeast food, super resistant malolactic bacteria, rack and return all worked with winemakers to create wines unlike any that had gone before.

Invention and progress is new for a limited time. That time gets shorter and shorter as information gets disseminated quicker and quicker. Halfway through the first decade of the new millennium, things are happening so fast that Jake Lorenzo can't even figure out what the far-fetched ideas are. One thing I do know, people are not likely to go back. Resist as much as you like, but the new technologies are here to stay.

We all share the tendency to look back fondly on what was before. We like to think that native yeast is more natural and therefore a better choice than manufactured yeast. We think that aging red wine in old barrels and racking every two months provides for gentle oxygenation and is the best way to soften tannins. We like to punch down in our open-topped fermenters because it gives us a link to winemakers from past centuries.

In the not too distant future, winemakers are likely to look at punching down and racking barrels the same way we now look at racking by the full moon. For Jake Lorenzo, it doesn't make any difference. Just take your far-fetched idea and get there by any means necessary. If you want to bubble oxygen through your wine while it puddles around a pile of oak chips; go for it. If you think grapes need to get very high sugars, have brown seeds and exhibit shriveled skins before harvest; then use the reverse osmosis system to make the very best wine you can. If you are after a well-made wine, produced from ripe fruit that still expresses its special terroir; then go make it.

Jake Lorenzo reminds you that the one unchanging aspect of wine is its diversity. Each wine is different from every other wine. I don't think that science, technology or voodoo will change that. And since people have varied tastes, there will always be some sort of market for all of those different wines.

When I'm listening to the crashing surf behind Chuy's Palapa Wine Bar munching on a hot steaming elote and sipping on a crisp, dry glass of Gewürztraminer, I hope no one comes up to me to say, "The waves are awesome Dude, but I miss the dusty, hot summers of my childhood."

Steroids For
The Vineyard

"Of course I know about it," brags Dr. Iggy Calamari inventor of the wine-powered pacemaker. "Hell, I sold them the damn machine."

"What machine?" inquires Jake Lorenzo, the naive private eye from Sonoma.

Calamari sighs, and then as if explaining to a forgetful child, "The Inductively-Coupled Plasma Spectrometer (ICPS). Damn thing's the size of a small pick up truck. With it we can provide a multi-element analysis measuring trace minerals and toxic metals. The ICPS takes the sample, blood or urine, either or the both. It heats the sample up to 17,000°F, which excites the atoms and emits energy wavelengths that are then captured and analyzed in parts per million."

"And athletes understand all that?" Jake asks.

"Certainly not," huffs the good doctor. "That's the whole point. Most athletes are not our best and our brightest. They don't go to work for NASA when they retire. Athletes are focused and concentrated on one thing: themselves. They're young, rich, inexperienced and terrified of failure. They are desperate to find an edge, to do what others do, to succeed.

"We simplify everything for them. We explain it in the simplest of terms, but you need the fancy machines, the scientific terminology, and the hocus pocus to suck them in. Remember, they have money and they are insecure. There have always been entrepreneurs waiting to help people like that spend their money."

The baseball season had started and Jake Lorenzo was trying to get a handle on this whole steroid controversy. I went to Dr. Iggy Calamari, a long-time friend and world famous scientist for information. He started with a history lesson. He told me that as far back as the fifth century athletes were looking for an edge. They would eat deer liver to give them speed, and they'd eat lion heart for strength. Ever since then athletes have experimented with training techniques, diet, drugs, vitamins, chemistry and even blood doping looking to get stronger or faster or quicker. (Jake noted that none of these things were purported to make athletes smarter.)

According to Dr. Calamari, rigorous exercise and stress can result in loss of important minerals and nutrients. People need something to replace those lost nutrients. Recently, anabolic steroids have been the popular choice, first with body builders, and then with other athletes. The steroids help build muscle mass, enhance strength and endurance, and speed up healing and recovery. Unfortunately, steroids have some nasty side effects like growing breasts on men and shriveling testicles to the size of shot berries in a Merlot cluster.

That's where companies like BALCO come in. Using their fancy ICPS, they take a test and show the client his or her mineral deficiencies. Their advisors set up a personalized training program to develop the specific skills of an athlete, and they advise on a series of supplements like androstenedione (andro), which is a natural form of steroid made from plants, and therefore not technically an anabolic steroid. They explain these supplements are natural and safe, but they are not cheap.

"It's snake oil, Jake," explains Dr. Calamari. "It's expensive, sounds simple, has a scientific background and seems to work. It's natural, safe (at least nobody's proved different) and the more you take the better it is. The more you take the richer the huckster gets."

"So, you're selling this andro to athletes?" I cry.

Iggy gives a smirk. "Let me say two words my master detective, 'Federal investigation.' I'm a scientist; I sold them the ICPS, took my money and got the hell out. Besides I found something much more lucrative, and far less controversial. Basically I sell steroids for grapevines."

Jake Lorenzo has to confess, I instinctively reached for my gun. First, Calamari messes with my beloved baseball, and now he's jerking around with my wine. I should kill the bastard and put an end to this blasphemy. Instead I take a few deep breaths, grit my teeth and wait for his explanation.

Steroids for the Vineyards

Iggy told me how grape growers in the seventies and early eighties were learning as they went. Most of them farmed apples, pears and prunes before trying grapes as a crop. They sprayed all sorts of stuff on the grapes and into the ground. They strip sprayed under the vines, disked between rows, and foliar sprayed for leafhoppers, dust mites and all sorts of insects. All of this spraying and disking quickly depleted the soils, so fertilizers became popular, and developed into big business.

By the mid-eighties grape farming was booming, and competition for farming dollars got fierce. The large pharmaceutical companies had a lock on most of the fertilizers until enterprising scientists started pushing organics. The organics people rejected chemical fertilizers, advocated cover crops and developed the first magic salable item: compost.

From there they were off to the races. Using petiole analysis (a fancy scientific test), farmers could determine mineral deficiencies and locate toxic metals in their soils. Organic salesmen gave them a wide range of choices. They said composting was natural, safe and efficient. Farmers could use fish emulsion or fish powder, compost teas made from a variety of manures, dried blood, bat guano and worm castings. Winery waste like pomace and stems could be utilized provided farmers used the proper techniques like turning the piles, stacking them in a certain way, adding various nutrients, and maintaining enough humidity.

Salesmen told eager farmers that they needed both growth and fruit enhancing nutrients, and that with proper use of organics, farmers could determine or influence flowering, fruit set, fruit size and vegetative growth. They could replenish the soil, make their grapevines stronger, more vigorous and more resistant to insect damage and disease.

Iggy had a glint in his eye as he explained how organic farming evolved into sustainable farming, which led to biodynamic farming. Biodynamics is a holistic system that includes livestock and takes into account the sun, moon and planets. Biodynamic growers try to produce everything in the vineyard. For example, sheep graze in the vineyards after harvest, eating the cover crop and adding manure to the soil. Biodynamic vintners say their wines have better balance, improved texture, darker color, deeper flavor, more power and greater density.

Most controversial in biodynamics is the use of eight soil and plant amendments numbered from 500 to 507. Iggy smiles with glee as he describes preparation 500. "We take cow manure, pack it into a female cow horn and bury it on the autumnal solstice for six months. We dig it up at the spring solstice, mix it with a lot of water and spray it over the soil." Preparation 501 is ground horn silica that is scattered on the plants. Preparations 502 through 507 are various plant substances like stinging nettles and yarrow blossom in a cow's udder. These are then added to compost. Farmers can prepare these preparations themselves or they can buy them. They are natural and safe, but they are not cheap.

Iggy reminds me that what goes around comes around. Now, in addition to natural compost, preparations buried on the solstice and crop management, there is new interest in chemistry. Potassium foliar sprays are being used to hasten ripening and increase color. Foliar boron is touted as helping with cell wall strength, cell division, fruit and seed development and sugar transport within the vine.

"Wineries and grape growers have huge investments, the competition is fierce and they are terrified of failure," Iggy explains. "They are desperate to find an edge, to do what others do, to succeed. It's all smoke and mirrors. What we offer is expensive, sounds simple, has a scientific background and seems to work. It's natural, safe, and the more you use the better it is. Remember, they have money and they are insecure. We are always willing to help people like that spend their money. We just have to get them to believe."

Jake Lorenzo had a headache. I could feel essential minerals depleting out of my body. I got out of Dr. Calamari's lab and hustled over to Chuy's Burrito Palace. I started on my own personalized regimen of taco, hot sauce and tequila. I did three reps. I felt a lot better.

The VinomAter®

"**W**histling while you work?" asked Jake Lorenzo, private eye. "It's happy work," replied Dr. Iggy Calamari, inventor of the wine-powered pacemaker. Iggy was whistling the UB40 version of *Red, Red Wine*, while he tinkered with his machine and said, "I've really got something here, Jake. If I can get this thing to work, I'll make so much money, it'll make my pacemaker royalties look like chump change." Iggy poured a five-gallon carboy of Cabernet Sauvignon into a stainless steel spout attached to his latest invention.

"Whew," I commented, "that wine's a little funky. I can smell the VA and the H_2S all the way over here."

"Not to worry," smiled Iggy, "when my VinomAter® (pronounced vin-o-mate-er like terminater) gets through with this, you're going to love it."

Iggy typed furiously on the keyboard, which was connected to a computer, which was connected to his VinomAter®. He whistled Dolly Parton's version of *Stairway to Heaven* as he pulled levers, closed up the machine and hit the start button.

Now, Jake Lorenzo is no scientist, but Dr. Calamari could be onto something big. His VinomAter® combines the latest wine technologies to turn plonk into 100 point monster wines. Iggy developed a program that profiles all the compounds found in wines that score 95 or above. He fed all of that information into his computer. The VinomAter® is basically a reverse osmosis filtration, but one that selectively removes compounds and rearranges molecules into other compounds that imitate the particular wine he's programmed into the machine.

According to the good Dr. Calamari, he can select a wine, say the 1996 Bryant Family Cabernet Sauvignon. He programs the characteristics of that wine, runs the plonk through the VinomAter® and ends up with something that tastes exactly like the wine he's selected. Using different programs, he can push out a clone of the 2000 Chapoutier Ermitage Cuvee del'Oree, or if you prefer he'll make a 1947 Cheval Blanc.

I sit at a counter, where Iggy blindfolds me and puts three glasses in front of me. He hands me the first glass. I taste it. Damn! It tastes exactly like the 2000 Chapoutier. The second glass tastes rich and huge. It has to be the Bryant Family Cabernet. I moan slightly as I sip the last wine, the 1947 Cheval Blanc, my birth year no less. It is sumptuous, rich, fully developed and soft as silk.

Jake Lorenzo sits there enjoying the aftertaste of that magnificent Cheval Blanc when a nasty thought pushes its way into my brain. Of course, Calamari is screwing with me. He's poured the real wines into the glasses. The VinomAter® is a sham.

I whip off the blindfold to see Iggy beaming. "Well, what do you think Mr. Private Eye?"

I look down at the three glasses. Each of them is filled with pink liquid. I re-taste the first glass. Once again, I get the intense peppery fruit of the Chapoutier. Open-jawed, I stare at Iggy and stutter, "But they're pink."

Iggy suppresses a grin. "Well, I'm still in the experimental stages. For some reason the reverse osmosis can't perform all the functions without removing the color. I'm pretty sure it has something to do with the anthocyanins."

I taste the Bryant Cabernet. "This is amazing. I can't believe that you turned that nasty plonk into this"

Iggy demurs modestly. "It's not that big a deal. Simple science, really, mixed with a little technology. My biggest problem is that it took all five gallons of that wine to make these three glasses."

"Yeah," I exclaim, "but plonk is cheap and what would a bottle of 1947 Cheval Blanc cost on today's market?" I mentally compute how much money I can free up to invest in Iggy's invention. "Geez, if you could make these machines small enough to fit in someone's home, people could dial in whatever wine they dreamed of tasting and have it whenever they wanted."

"That's right," agreed Iggy, "and there would be no bottles, no corks, no TCA and no need for storage. Unfortunately, this prototype cost $6 million so far. I doubt that the VinomAter® will find its way into too many homes."

"But giant corporations like Constellation, Diageo or Beringer Blass could pony up. $6 million is chump change to those boys." I gush. "But you will have to fix the color thing. No one is going to spend $6 million for rosé."

Later that night Jakelyn's mother and I are seated on the porch looking at the garden. I pull the cork on a homemade Pinot Noir and wonder about the future. The wine is lovely, with aromas of dried cherries and flavors of ripe plum. I gaze out into the garden looking at the glory of the dahlias: giant purple dahlias the size of soft balls, red dahlias the color of claret, and yellow dahlias that look like exploding fireworks.

I remind myself that nature is magical, and that magic is something I love. Magic is predicated on things we do not understand. Once you know how something works, the magic disappears.

Jake Lorenzo is a private eye. It's my business to look into the abyss, to find the truth, to learn how a thing works. Early on, I learned not to look too closely at the things I loved. For example, I love to cook, but I've resisted learning cooking secrets from chefs because I don't want to lose the "magic" I find in cooking a good meal. I love making my homemade wine, but I don't want to get too involved with the science of it for fear of losing the "magic" in the bottle.

Iggy Calamari is a scientist. Scientists spend their lives searching for answers. I think scientists find their "magic" in the search itself. Theirs is a personal, internal sort of journey. They often overlook the consequences their inventions exert on the rest of us.

Each of us has to decide how much science and technology we want in our lives, because the more science and technology we accept, the less magic we have left.

Jake Lorenzo can do without cell phones. Their intrusive nature overrides the convenience for this private eye. And I've decided I can live without Iggy's VinomAter®. I just don't want to forego that moment between pulling the cork and taking that first sip. The surprise of youthful fruit in an old bottle, or even the disappointment of a Ribero del Duero loaded with Brett. It's the not knowing that makes wine a mystery, one that we can solve each night with a simple corkscrew.

I can see the seductive quality of Iggy's invention. I can understand people deciding to use it. I will never forget the taste of that 1947 Cheval Blanc he made. But, at this point in my life, I'll stick with the uncertainty of my wine cellar and my trusty corkscrew. And I don't care how sublime the wine from Iggys's VinomAter®, he ain't gonna make it if the wine is pink.

Wine Time

Jake Lorenzo could barely squeeze through the dozens of free-standing clocks. Pendulum clocks, cuckoo clocks, and electronic clocks made out of every conceivable wood, metal and modern plastic substance were jammed into Dr. Iggy Calamari's living room. Every square inch of wall space in the hallway and guest bedroom was covered with wall clocks. Art deco clocks, cartoon faced clocks, giant numbered clocks adorned every square inch of every wall. Every drawer, cabinet and counter in the kitchen was dotted with watches. Wrist watches, pocket watches, digital watches, waterproof watches all sparkled and blinked the time.

Dr. Iggy Calamari stood in front of the stove trying to push through a pile of battery operated alarm clocks to make room for the coffee pot. His hair stuck out wildly from his head. His blood-shot eyes glared from under half-closed lids. Dark circles slid from under his eyes onto rough-hewn stubble. He kept scratching his forearm with trembling fingers. "It's the ticking, Jake. The damn ticking gets into your head and under your skin. I can literally feel time crawling around under my skin. I'm close to a break through, I know it."

Jake Lorenzo, private eye, swept a pile of Mickey Mouse watches off a kitchen chair. I gently placed my arm around Calamari's shoulder and guided him to the chair. I took the coffee pot off the fire and filled it with water, something Calamari had overlooked. "Iggy," I said, "You look like a winemaker who's just had a giant outbreak of lactobacillus. You look like a grower with an infestation of vine mealy bug. Hell, you look like Saddam Hussein when he crawled out of the hole. What the hell is going on here?"

"Time, Jake," he shuddered. "Time is going on, and on and on. It never stops. And it keeps going faster and faster. Nobody notices. I've got to make them understand." Calamari put his head in his hands, and started to sob. Then he fell asleep.

I dragged the good doctor through the labyrinth of free-standing clocks, down the hallway jammed with wall clocks and into his bedroom filled with digital alarm clocks. I placed him on the bed, placed all of the alarm clocks into a dresser drawer and lugged it out to the garage. I went back to the bedroom, placed a blanket over his comatose body and left, closing the bedroom door behind me.

Dr. Iggy Calamari, inventor of the wine-powered pacemaker, has become obsessed with time. Iggy thinks that time goes faster and faster the older we get. When it overtakes us we die. Iggy figures if we can slow speeding time, we can achieve immortality.

Now, Jake Lorenzo longs for a good $10 bottle of red wine. I long to see the Chicago Cubs win a World Series. I long to see Jakelyn's daughter get over her fixation for toe socks, but I don't long for immortality. Immortality is too permanent, and one thing detectives have learned is that nothing is ever permanent.

Recently, Jakelyn's mom and I visited friends in Louisiana. I found myself in a wonderful, privately-owned grocery market that has one of the most incredible wine departments anywhere. This single store averages close to $9 million in sales per year. The manager, an old friend of almost fifteen years confided to me, "I don't drink much wine anymore. I've switched to vodka. The wine guys have no more soul. It's just 'turn and burn' with them. Their time has come and gone."

Jake Lorenzo knows the wine business. Winemakers and cellar rats are dedicated hard-working people, but they focus so hard on what they are doing, they concentrate so much on the details of making wine, growing grapes and new technologies that the outside business world passes them over. Time whizzes by. Crush moves to barreling down to racking to bottling. One vintage runs into the next.

When they finally get a chance to break loose, when they take the time to look around, they see giant distributors like Southern, Glazers, and Magnolia have gobbled up small independent distributors all across the nation. They notice that Diageo, Southcorp, and Constellation have bought out wineries large and small; turning them into commodities just like car insurance or widgets. They realize that their own most famous brands have turned arrogant and expensive and are no longer viable for the wine-drinking public. If they are smart, they realize that they have not put in the time to maintain relationships, and they understand that they are under attack.

When wine reps take the time to go back on the road they find that their best lieutenants, the individual wine salespeople are being hung out to dry. They hear one horror story after another about how distributors have screwed individual salesmen with their acquisitions and reorganizations. It's gotten so bad that individual sales people, faced with cut territories and decreased sales commissions, have to beg their customers to fight on their behalf.

Wine sales people are foot soldiers for independent wineries. The only way to get past the giant supplier conglomerates and their quotas and spiffs and pressure is to cultivate sales people to sell your product. Wineries need to invest the time to build relationships. They need to rebuild the links between the individual sales people and their customers. They need to join the alliance between the sales people and their buyers and help them defend against the onslaught of corporate wine sales.

Sales people are time-crunched. They have supervisors, sales managers, and customers all vying for their time. They have a foot up their butts and someone looking over their shoulder. When you are doing your ride-withs, stop focusing on moving boxes, writing the order and making the sale. Take some time to get to know your sales force. Listen to their complaints, problems and concerns. Spend some social time with them and their customers, away from the store. Build relationships with them, help defend them against the conglomerates and they will reward you by championing your brand.

The wine business is no longer the idyllic pastoral haven it once was. The onslaught of technology and the pace of business have forced a quantum leap forward. As a business, wine is stuck in fast forward. It is time to slow down and re-establish personal relationships.

You have two choices: either make the time to build relationships and get back to the basics of selling, or count on Dr. Iggy Calamari to come up with some time slowing invention that will give you some measure of immortality.

Given that the police radio in my car is squawking about a swat team being pelted with alarm clocks in a standoff outside the good Doctor's house, Jake Lorenzo recommends you go with the first choice.

Competition

Iggy Calamari called to give me a warning. "Jake, you got some private eye competition in your hometown, Sonoma," he said, "and she's good looking and friendly as hell."

Jake Lorenzo has lived in Sonoma for 33 years. There's nowhere near enough investigative work for even one detective to make a living. It's bad enough I've got to take on sleazy cases for winery owners insecure about their married relationships. I get queasy every time the bare larder forces me to take on bodyguard duty for some drug-crazed rock and roller, or even worse, some pampered starlet with her silicone breasts hanging out of a skin-tight bodysuit. Now, I'm going to have to share the meager work with some other detective. I don't think so.

I hustled over to Calamari's. No one answered my knock, but the door was unlocked so I went in. The coffee pot was still on and I thought I heard some noise coming from Calamari's lab. I walked quietly across the yard toward the lab when suddenly I was bowled over from behind. Someone jumped on my chest and I was slapped in the face by something cold, wet and sticky.

"I see you've met Ziggy," Calamari laughed.

I looked up to see an eager golden lab waiting attentively next to my prone body. Her eyes were focused on the slobber-covered tennis ball that had rolled off my cheek and was lying on the ground between us. As I sat up and reached for the ball, the dog perked her ears in anticipation. I tossed the ball with a lot of force. The dog was off like a bullet, leaping up and snatching the ball in mid-air. She was back, dropping the ball at my feet as I stood up. "Pretty impressive," I commented.

The dog alertly kept shifting her gaze between me and the ball, but Jake Lorenzo didn't want to spend the rest of his life tossing tennis balls to a retriever, no matter how adept that retriever might be. I shuffled away from the ball and toward Calamari. "I didn't know you were into dogs, Iggy."

"Well, Ziggy is much more than a regular dog," said Calamari evidently slipping the dog some special signal because she immediately heeled behind him as we walked to the lab. "Ziggy is a detective and a very good one."

"This is the competition you were talking about?" I asked, relieved that my limited income sources were evidently safe.

"Indeed she is. Ziggy is a trained TCA detective. Periodically, I need to put her through her paces to keep her up to the task." Calamari explained that a dog's sense of smell is 400 times greater than a human's. When you take a wonderful animal like Ziggy, with a pedigree that would evidently put any of us to shame, and train her to retrieve something special, then she gets very good at it. Retrieving is in their DNA and when trained properly, dogs just want to be rewarded with love.

Calamari was looking for something to do with his spare time so he bet some other scientist that he could train a dog to seek out tiny amounts of 2,4,6-tricholoroanisole (TCA). Most people know TCA as "cork taint." When we say a bottle is corked, it's because we are picking up aromas from the TCA compound. TCA is formed when naturally-occurring airborne fungi come into contact with chlorophenol compounds. Sometimes, chlorine used in cleaning corks links up with these fungi and we can get cork taint.

Unfortunately, TCA can also be systemic. Systemic TCA infects wineries by means other than cork and can affect an entire winery's production. Wine barrels, drain pipes, rubber hoses and even gaskets can be infected by TCA. Usually, systemic TCA infects wines in such tiny amounts that the consumer is not likely to pick it up, but put systemic TCA infected wine into bottles topped with even slightly tainted corks and all hell breaks loose.

Iggy figured if he could train a dog to sniff out TCA, it would help wineries locate sources of infection. Barrel makers and oak alternative producers could check their aging piles of wood and be sure they were uninfected. Cork suppliers could have the dog root through their batches of corks and locate problematic stoppers.

"She was such a great dog," Iggy smiled. "I started with a rag dipped in some TCA solution. I'd let her smell it and then toss it. She'd retrieve it. I'd pat her on the head, give her some verbal love and toss the rag again. Over time, I lowered the amount of TCA on the rag, then we dispensed with the rag and used a tainted piece of oak. Once she got used to retrieving the oak, I started hiding it. She would run frantically in a zig-zag pattern until she found it, and then she'd come running to give it to me. That's why I named her Ziggy. It was all that zig-zagging she'd do. By the time I finished, Ziggy could find TCA taint as low as 3 parts per billion."

Ziggy was occasionally brought in by wineries and barrel makers to locate TCA infection, but frankly, there just wasn't a lot of work to be had. Jake Lorenzo shared a knowing look at Ziggy, as one struggling detective to another. As good as she was at her job, she remained a well-kept secret within the wine business, because no one wanted to be associated with TCA and "cork taint."

The real problem was that Calamari was always traveling to some science convention or working on a project abroad. There was too much alone time for a dog, especially one as special as Ziggy. "I found a good family for Ziggy," Calamari assured me. "Why don't you come with me and meet them at their new tasting salon?"

We drove into Sonoma, where just 1/2 block from the Sonoma plaza on East Napa St. was the brand new Sojourn Tasting Salon. Sojourn Cellars is a partnership between Craig Haserot and winemaker Erich Bradley. They focus on limited hand-crafted, artisanal wine, mostly Pinot Noir along with some Cabernet Sauvignon. Craig and his wife Ellen run the tasting salon. Ziggy bounds to Craig when he appears, dropping a tennis ball at his feet. Craig picks it up and tosses it, hitting the side of the building. Ziggy is back in a flash. Craig throws the ball again hitting a sign with a loud clang.

"I hope he makes wine better than he can throw a tennis ball," I confided to Iggy.

Once inside the warm salon with its dark wood floors and its massive wood tasting table, we are treated to an extensive tasting. We taste three 2006 Pinot Noirs, four 2007 Pinots and three different Cabernet Sauvignons. I was enthralled with the Pinots, especially the 2007 vintage. They were lush, complex and subtle with all the charm of fine Pinot Noir. Craig was knowledgeable and opinionated about his wines. By the time Calamari and I left, we knew a lot about Sojourn Cellars and had tasted a batch of delicious wine.

If you'd like to visit the salon, it's open daily by appointment. Just call (707) 938-7212 for a reservation. If, while you are tasting those delightful wines, you feel a wet, slimy ball being pushed into your lap, then you have just met Ziggy, Sonoma's other great detective.

Out of Tune

Jake Lorenzo is hurting. I'm trying to recover from a four-day binge of laughter-filled gluttony and revelry, the likes of which happen at our house with severe regularity. This time started in San Francisco where we went to see the gifted Judy Kaye in *Souvenir: A Fantasia on the Life of Florence Foster Jenkins*. It was a bewitching, hilarious near-perfect afternoon of theater.

Ms. Jenkins was a real woman, a wealthy society lady who lived in New York in the 1930s and 40s. She loved music and fancied herself a supremely talented coloratura soprano. Unfortunately, she had no sense of pitch or tone and basically couldn't sing a lick. She was to singing what an over-oaked, malolactic Chardonnay bomb is to winemaking. And true to the metaphor, Ms. Jenkins became wildly popular.

The play tells her story from the point of view of one Cosme McMoon, Ms. Jenkins's accompanist. Appalled by her tonal-challenged screeching, he nevertheless comes to appreciate her love for what she does and her unwavering confidence in her own ability. This makes for one incredibly funny play while still delivering a good many themes for the audience to ponder.

If someone approaches their art with all of their heart and soul, does it matter whether or not they have any talent? If Florence Foster Jenkins sang so horribly that her audience had tears rolling down their cheeks from desperately trying *not* to laugh, did that mean that the singer was wrong to assume that her voice had moved them to tears? If Ms. Jenkins heard herself as perfectly in tune, with emotional renderings of classic songs then who's to say that she was mistaken?

Is there any difference between a singer who can't sing and a winemaker who lets grapes hang until the grapes reach 30°Brix, then dilutes with water, removes alcohol with reverse osmosis, stores the wine in a tank with oak chips, bubbles oxygen through it and then promotes it as the finest wine in the land? Which of the two is the most delusional? Are those tears of repressed laughter or have they moved you to crying?

Jake Lorenzo's liver may be crying, but my soul is filled with joy. The aforementioned Judy Kaye, along with her husband and two other actor friends just spent four days with us. Once again, Jakelyn's mother and I got to introduce wonderful people to our Wine Country life-style. One night we started with Champagne and caviar. We moved on to Sauvignon Blanc and tuna sashimi and then opened Pinot Noirs to go with the grilled pompano. From there we sampled a couple of rich young Cabernet Sauvignons and finished with a magnum of older Relentless Merlot alongside a platter of fine cheeses.

Our guests became giddy with the flavors. They thrilled to the sounds of popping corks. They savored the pairings of wine and food. They discussed the wines and were enraptured by their complexity and depth of flavor. We went late into the night telling jokes and stories, which become so much more entertaining with actors because they use accents and voices, gestures and pacing to heighten every punch line.

The next morning we went to Imagery to taste wine and look at the art. From there we met up with Chuy at the Burrito Palace and he toured us through the Mexican markets and the weekend burrito wagons to select a diverse sampling of Mexican delights. We devoured the food on the porch gazing upon the glorious blooms of Jakelyn's mother's garden. I took them to Artesa for some afternoon wine tasting. It was crystal clear with pristine views all the way back to San Francisco. The hills were vibrant with lush green grasses and dappled by bursts of bright yellow Acacia.

Dinner started with homemade country paté, followed by a sparkling green chili flan that led to braised lamb shanks over homemade noodles. I sent them time after time to the wine cellar to pick out whatever struck their fancy. Before the night was over we had visited Argentine Malbec, Chilean Carmenere, the French Cote Rotie, Tuscan Chianti and Sicilian Nero di Avola. Once again, we went late into the night singing along with records while we sipped at various Grappas and Mezcals.

We took advantage of the glorious weather on Sunday to wander through the neighborhood. We gazed at the views and I regaled them of stories about the old days in the wine business. I told them about hijacking the Wine Train, kidnapping Richard Branson and Crush party tradition. I introduced them to window diving while we sipped afternoon Ghalarifies at the Swiss Hotel. I took them to special vineyards tucked in the hills where they could look down upon serpentine rows of grapes and across the valley to Sonoma Mountain. They could see the majesty of Mt. Tam, the glitter of sunlight off the bay and the city outlines of both Oakland and San Francisco.

Back home that evening was a night of simple barbecue while we tasted through California Zinfandels. Then we moved to Syrahs and compared examples from Paso Robles, Napa and Washington. We brought out some Chateauneuf and Australian Shiraz and debated old world versus new world techniques.

For their final day, we sent them off to a golf course. They came back as excited as school children telling us about the hawk they saw in flight, describing the different trellising systems in the vineyards adjacent to the golf course and raving about the brisk clean air. We sat them down at the table and dumped out a Cajun style crab boil featuring local Dungeness crabs, artichokes and homemade sausage. We paired the spicy crab with bottle after bottle of dry Alsatian Gewürztraminer and watched their eyes go wide as they proclaimed, "This is a flavor match made in heaven."

While we sat in the living room realizing that this spectacular visit was coming to an end, they were effusive in their thanks, but they couldn't resist asking one question. "Do you eat and drink like this all the time?"

Jakelyn's mom looked at me, then grinned at them, "Pretty much."

The next day, when they had gone, I sat on the porch thinking about how fortunate we are to live here in the heart of Wine Country. Sometimes, our senses to the beauty around us become dulled by the daily repetition of living here. Taking people around and seeing where we live through their eyes, reopens ours. Serving them home cooked food and an unending line-up of fine wine, not only makes for entertaining evenings, but it reminds us of being hosted in places like France, Spain, Italy and Argentina.

For those of us in the business, Wine Country living can become old hat. We almost come to expect extraordinary hospitality when we are traveling to other countries and visiting other winemakers. For people not in the business, this kind of hospitality makes them incredulous and sparks promises of, "We've got to do this more often."

We were able to give our guests a few days that they will never forget. I have no doubt that they will soon entertain us in their home territory and we will have an ongoing long-lasting friendship. In the meantime, Jake Lorenzo needs to take a nap. Then I'll get up and pack my bag, because tomorrow we leave for New Orleans, where as far as I can tell they pretty much invented hospitality.

Sore Backs

Lorenzo Lavanderia has magic hands.

The masterful Uruguayan Laundromat operator with the incredible wine cellar came to Sonoma for a visit. It was his first trip to the United States and he stayed with us for a week. Jake Lorenzo sent him out each day to visit wineries, and then I'd cook elaborate dinners for him where he could meet invited guests at our house.

Lorenzo Lavanderia marveled at the weather, the rolling hillsides and the lack of grazing cattle. He reveled in the lush mouth-feel of Sonoma Chardonnays, the rich complexity of Russian River Pinots and the power of Napa Valley Cabernets. He loved the intricate dinners at our table, the varied guests and the array of wines that we consumed from all parts of the world. He was elated by the neighborhood burrito wagons and treasured our nightly 2 AM hot tubs.

But it wasn't all good for him. The paucity of Laundromats put him in a deep funk and their grimy, worn and tattered look made him cringe. Twice we had to take him to the coast. "I'm Uruguayan," he explained, "I can't be away from the water too long." The first time he saw wine prices here, he got lightheaded and almost fainted. Fortunately Jake Lorenzo had a flask of tequila and I was able to revive him. He took the flask with him on his daily excursions to wineries.

One day, toward the end of his visit, he was helping me load rocks into my truck to take back to Jakelyn's mother's garden. I attempted to lift too large a stone and my back tweaked. By the time we finished, it was all I could do to stand up straight.

Lorenzo Lavanderia took me inside, had me lie down on the floor and worked on me for 10 minutes. The pain was gone. "It's just a personalized version of Somatics," he explained. "You work in the laundry business, hauling heavy bags of laundry, bent over pushing clothes into machines, then you know about back pain." Somatics, semantics. Jake Lorenzo says he has magic hands.

Frankly, there is not a lot of heavy lifting in detective work. Occasionally, some muscle-bound clown will hassle you, but that can usually be deflected by quickness and balance. Sitting in cars on a stake-out for long periods of time can stiffen your muscles, but a few stretches takes care of that. No, detective work is not the culprit. Jake Lorenzo's back troubles are directly related to my 32 years of making wine.

Actor Dennis Hopper once said, "If you say you remember the 60s, then you weren't there."

Jake Lorenzo says, "If you're a long-time winemaker and your back doesn't hurt, then someone else has been making your wine for you."

There are winemakers and there are winemakers. Some winemakers have to worry about severe paper cuts from passing out work orders. Others are concerned about carpal tunnel syndrome from spending all that time at their computer screens. Winemakers suffer a lot of stress trying to get other people to pick up checks for their extravagant lunches. I know winemakers who have bad knees because of all the time they spend begging for money from their bankers. None of these guys have bad backs.

Then there are winemakers who actually wear out their rubber boots. The ones who are the first into a tank to shovel out red pomace when there is no oxygen to breathe. Winemakers who move two cases of wine at a time in some hysterical, macho concept of speed and pride. Winemakers who haul hoses and full buckets and sacks of DE. Winemakers who roll gas cylinders, drag pumps up hills and pull machines over obstacles. These people all have bad backs.

There's the people lifting barrels, using chains to move full barrels that have tumbled off their racks and climbing like monkeys five barrels high to top up. There are winemakers who spend 10 hours a day walking in rubber boots on cold cement floors in the winter while tanks are covered with cold stabilization ice. Their fingers are numb with the cold while they grasp icy stainless steel clamps, their hands freeze while they mix up additions and their ears ring with the crash of calving ice as the tanks defrost. These are the people with bad backs.

There are pickers hauling full lug boxes over uneven terrain. Pruners bent over vines pulling leaves or suckers or dropping green fruit. There are people setting posts, pulling wire and hooking up the drip lines. They can all expect back trouble.

Back trouble isn't the only thing that long-time winemakers have to worry about. Remember when we used to chlorine the floors every Friday? That chlorine and wine acid combined to make some pungent, nasal draining, eye watering chlorine gas. How about pumping over a tank and getting hit with CO_2 so hard that it snaps your head back like an Evander Holyfield jab. Nothing that smells as nasty and burns your throat as much as SO_2 can be good for you. This stuff may not hurt your back, but it will take a toll.

Let's face it. If you were making wine in the 70s or even the 80s, nobody was forcing you to do this stuff. Hell, we reveled in it. We were tough and strong. We were invincible. We could work all day and party all night. We used chlorine gas like fops in the Renaissance used snuff. We could live on CO_2 fumes from a red wine tank and fill a six-ton press in 15 minutes. We could punch down tanks until our muscles bulged like Arnold Schwarzenegger when he was on steroids.

Nowadays it hurts when I pick up rocks. Punching down gives me stomach cramps. Making simple SO_2 additions to my barrels makes me cough like a life-long smoker. I have to rest in between hauling lug boxes and I only move one full case of wine at a time.

"Why do we do it?" you might be asking.

Jake Lorenzo will tell you why. We do it for the high. We love the wine buzz. We like the way it makes us feel, the way it enhances a good meal and the way it boosts a conversation. We do it because there is a real sense of pride in taking something that grows on a plant and turning it into something magical that we can share with our friends. In this high-tech world where most people are service providers, there is something very special about producing something of our own. Sometimes a little wine (and the right pill) can even help a sore back.

Jake Lorenzo is not one of those guys who says, "If I'd have known I was going to live this long, I'd have taken better care of myself." Screw that. There are no guarantees when it comes to the time we've got. I say use it while you've got it, but if you live long enough to get back pains, then you could do a lot worse than having a Uruguayan Laundromat operator with magic hands for a friend.

The Dance

In the Dark

Grapevines

Terroir

Harvest

Wine Appreciation 101

Tell Me A Story

Variety Is the Spice of Life

Jake's on the Case

Peace on Earth

On the Passing of Dreams

The Dance

Jake Lorenzo pours a shot of Herradura Blanco into his morning coffee and watches mesmerized as Chuy works in the kitchen. The Burrito Palace is buzzing with the morning breakfast rush, so Chuy Palacios is in the weeds. He cuts three rectangular slices of steaming chilaquiles and puts them on plates. Cracking eggs into a pan he tosses the shells into the garbage bin without looking. He whips around, spoons a pile of beans onto each plate and while putting the bean pot back with his right hand, sprinkles cotija cheese on top with his left. He slides one egg onto each of the chilaquiles, ladles his glorious green chile on top and hits the bell.

"Listo," he shouts and the waitress is gone with the plates while Chuy glides into more orders glancing at the tickets hanging above the stove, whirling his arms and filling plates effortlessly. It's a marvelous dance; each step choreographed with no wasted motion and completed plates of gorgeous food appearing as if by magic and then being hustled off by the waitress before you can get a good look to figure out the illusion.

Chuy has told me that cooking through a rush is like working in slow motion. Once he hits that groove, everything is right there before him in perfect sequence. He describes it as an "out of body" experience. Instant art on a plate, readily devoured and with no proof of the art ever existing except in the satisfied expressions on the customers faces as they leave the Burrito Palace.

Jake Lorenzo looks around the restaurant. The clientele is divided between Mexicano laborers, Sonoma Valley retirees and bleary eyed winemakers reveling in an early morning hot meal of subtle, mouth tingling, complex flavors.

Much like Chuy in the kitchen, Jake Lorenzo has witnessed the winemaker dance at many a winery. That exhausted winemaker munching on Chuy's chilaquiles and slurping down his breakfast molé enchiladas will soon be higher than a kite in an oxygen deprived tank surrounded by the incredible fruit-fermented aromas of red wine. He'll shovel grapes out of a tank as fast as he can while his heart pumps madly until he stops to stick his head outside the tank and drink in a sweet hit of oxygen.

As sublime as Chuy's green chile is, Jake Lorenzo doubts that there is anything more delicious than the aromas wafting off a clean, red wine fermentation. The dance of trucks and forklifts and workers as grapes are dumped into the crusher is every bit as intricate as the steps practiced by Chuy at a breakfast rush. Cellar rats rushing around on catwalks, switching valves and moving hoses to some invisible pattern creates an energy and drama that is palpable, even to the tourists rolling up in their groups and being fed a canned speech by their guide.

During harvest there is an un-ending, never-diminishing pressure. No matter how hard or fast winemakers move they fall behind. No matter how organized and ready a winemaker might be, the input of data is sure to overwhelm. The 20 tons of Pinot Noir from such and such a vineyard turns out to be a mere 12, so now it is in a half-filled tank. The Sauvignon Blanc crushed last week is still not fermenting vigorously. Something is wrong with the refrigeration system, the forklift is leaking hydraulic oil and for no reason the water just shut off.

The assistant winemaker has just screamed at the cellar master to jump into the open fermenter of Pinot Noir and never come out. The cute young intern from Spain is quietly sobbing behind tank #3 while the lab tech's dog is humping the leg of the manager of the biggest on-premise account from St. Louis. The guest chef cooking lunch for the crew is in a panic because he thought you said he'd be cooking for two, when the real number is 42.

The forecasters say a heat wave is coming, but a check of the charts shows there are only two empty tanks left. A third of the brand new barrels are leaking like colanders, so they'll need another day before they can be filled. Acids are very high and so is pH. Sugars are up and malolactic fermentations are sluggish. Someone forgot to ice down the beer, and some clown from the health department has just shown up for a surprise inspection. Oh, by the way, your wife called to ask you to pick up the kids from gymnastics class at four, and remind you that you're cooking dinner for the Seattle distributor's sales team at seven.

In the weeds is in the weeds, whether you are in a kitchen or a winery. The difference is a restaurant rush lasts about three hours. Harvest lasts eight weeks. There are chefs that scream and yell and throw knives. They disparage the help, increase the tension and complain about minor things. There are winemakers who get sullen, snipe at the cellar rats and take away beer rations citing insurance concerns.

Then there are chefs and winemakers who learn to dance.

They learn to take pressure and set-backs like a peyote trip with a Huichol shaman. Go with the flow. Open up to the unexpected and revel in every hallucinogenic vision that flashes in front of you. Conserve your energy, be efficient in your movements, watch things go into slow motion and use that vision to calm the troops.

Slap a King Sunny Ade disc into the player and fill the ice chest with water, toss in some CO_2 pellets and the beer is cold. Steer the inspector toward the tasting room where they've just remodeled and installed a new dishwasher. Give the chef some cash and a map to the market.

Perform a sweet two-step turn, toss the dog a piece of carnitas from someone's breakfast burrito and give the on-premise manager a cold beer. Ask the Chilean intern to talk to the Spanish intern, offer the forklift mechanic a magnum of the Private Reserve he likes to fix the forklift today, and tell the crew about the tank full of water you have as backup for when the well shuts down.

Cha-cha through your cell phone directory calling the refrigeration company and offering them your attorney's number and a lawsuit if they don't spring for overtime to have their mechanic in your winery within the next hour. Call the next door neighbor and ask if they can pick up your kids when they get theirs. Decide the Seattle crew would love to have a burrito wagon experience. Leave yourself a text message to pick up flowers for your wife.

When the day is over, get a good night's sleep and then go the Chuy's Burrito Palace for breakfast to watch a real master dance in the kitchen.

In The Dark

Detectives love the dark. We do some of our best work then. There is something about the lack of light that lends a simmering, sinister quality to our movements and thoughts, and this is the world detectives inhabit. Stakeouts are much easier at nighttime. The sleazebags tend to celebrate at night, so we can observe them. Infidelities prefer the cloak of darkness. Clandestine meetings almost always take place when it is dark.

Darkness enhances a lot of good things, too. A romantic candle-lit dinner loses impact in the daylight. A roaring fire works better at night. We watch movies in the dark. The burrito wagons don't get cranking until darkness falls. The moon is more dramatic at night.

Jake Lorenzo is a private eye, so it's natural that I love the dark. I'm also a wine drinker. When it comes to winemaking, I love a good cave.

Caves are to winemaking what "noir" is to movie making. Caves exude a humid, sticky, sensuality that ravages the senses and clings to the soul. Add the aromas of earth and wine, the sound of dripping water, the echo of the smallest movement, the mysterious muffling of damp air and you've got a salacious stew that stinks of romance, danger and magic.

Mankind has a long and abiding history with caves. When the first of our kind roamed the planet, they lived in caves. That's why we don't call them condominium men. When cavemen painted their houses, they stayed away from bright colors, crown moldings, and faux work. Instead they concentrated on murals. Their walls carried the record of their lives.

Wine was likely invented in a cave. It only makes sense that when cavemen first happened on wild fruit, they ate their fill. As the fruiting season waned, they must have picked all the fresh fruit they could and carried it to their cave homes hoping to eat it later in the winter. Somewhere in the dark coolness of a cave, some of that fruit started to ferment and when the cavemen ate that fruit and drank the resultant liquid, they got higher than monkeys in a banana orgy.

Years later, when cavemen moved into hovels, shacks, monasteries and castles, they still kept the magical fermented fruit products in their sacred caves. Is it not written that Friar Dom Perignon pulled a bottle of his fruit product out from its resting place in his cave, popped it open, and exclaimed, "I am drinking the stars." That's why to this day all of Champagne sits atop miles and miles of dark, dank, musty champagne caves. The French may not know much, but they know that stars come out at night, and if you want stars in bottles you better keep them in the dark.

The New World came into winemaking and wine caves pretty recently. Jacob Schram of Schramsberg Vineyards is credited with building the first wine cave in California. He used the same Chinese laborers who had brought the railroads out west, because John Henry had died and was no longer available. They dug the caves with picks and shovels and blasting powder.

Other winemakers must have thought Schram was nuts, because none of them got into caves for close to a hundred years. In 1981, Far Niente built a small cave, and the race was on. Today we have about 150 wine caves in Northern California Wine Country.

Building a cave is a relatively straight-forward job. You compose a basic layout, set a budget, hire a cave drilling company and have at it. Of course, the guys from the drilling company who speak to you, walk you through their other caves and haggle over price are not the guys who drill the cave. They are the owners and the salesmen who most likely will be on the golf course or the tennis courts while the actual work is being done.

The cave will be dug by the chief engineer and the muckers. Cave drillers are an unusual breed. They work hard, drink hard and fight hard. Theirs is a closed society that takes pride in its work, toils underground, and is adept at tasks that civilians know nothing about.

The drilling machine itself is so dangerous that it makes a Minestrine pump look like a child's bake oven. The rows of metal teeth sitting in the rounded drill bits spin at great speed, churning through the earth and rock pulverizing it to dust and chunks called muck. Metal conveyors carry the muck to small trucks that drive it out of the cave to the dump site. All this moving, spinning, grinding machinery is working in dirt and dust. It breaks often and usually in scary, dangerous ways.

At the end of each drilling day, muckers spray concrete on the walls to secure the cut and prevent cave-ins. The hose is heavy, full of dry concrete mix. The pressure is enormous; enough to push dry cement. The mix flies out of the hose through a mist of water until it sticks (hopefully) to the walls and ceiling. Inevitably chunks of wet concrete will fall. When they fall on the hose operator, he's knocked to the ground, breath gone with bones likely broken.

Once the cave is rough finished, the drains need to be dug, the electrical run, and the floor must be poured. After that, the crew comes back and sprays another, final coat of concrete on the walls.

If you own a winery and are considering a cave, Jake Lorenzo has some advice for you: hire or appoint a project manager. The project manager has three main duties.

First, you've got to be there. You can't know what's going on if you aren't around every day at different times. Second, you must take care of the crew. They are the ones doing the work. Beer after work, occasional meals, a fine dinner now and then are cheap investments when you need free advice over a problem area, or you'd like a small connecting tunnel dug at a very discounted price.

Finally, check the monthly billing. I'm not saying that drilling invoices aren't accurate, but cave company computer print outs make double billing by glass companies and distributors charging for display set ups pale in comparison. Go over those pages with a fine-toothed corkscrew. Mark in red all those charges for $1 nails, support wire that never got used and time the bosses say they were on site, when you know they were pool side. Trust Jake, you'll save $5,000-$10,000 per month if you are vigilant.

I've already told you why detectives like caves. Winemakers like caves because the high humidity environment cuts evaporative loss and actually lowers alcohol. Accountants like caves because the constant 58° F saves on air conditioning in the summer and on winter heating. Winery owners love caves because they look neat and allow them to spend fortunes to impress their friends. Wine drinkers like caves because they are dark, cold, and magical and remind them of the romance of wine, which is what interested them in the first place.

Jake's got another hint to save you money. Caves are like boats, the next guy always has a nicer one. If you think you are going to build the biggest, fanciest cave in the world, do yourself a favor. Go take a look at Jarvis Winery with its underground winemaking facility complete with waterfall and crystal room or go to Palmaz Winery and see what a five-story, state-of-the-art, engineered, gravity flow underground palace can look like.

Jake Lorenzo says you can catch as many fish off a row boat as you can off a yacht. Stick to a budget. Build a cave that suits your personality and your needs. After all, the main idea is to make better wine.

Grapevines

Jake Lorenzo spent a few hours walking through vineyards today. It's a wonderful time of year to wander the vineyards. Flowering is just finishing up, and the brilliant, almost electric green of new leaves and tendrils glows with healthy vigor. This week's hot weather along with the warm nights has the vines exploding with growth, just like the San Francisco Giants on their ten-game winning streak.

I think too many of us take these vineyards for granted. Jake Lorenzo sees you in your cars, on your cell phones scurrying down the roads on one errand or another. Traffic whizzes by on the highways, drivers glancing at the beauty of the rows of vines climbing the gentle hills, but seemingly more concerned with getting to their next appointment or getting the kids to the next lesson. Tourists marvel at the vineyards, but rarely venture off the highways to wander amongst the vines. Jake Lorenzo says you can't truly appreciate a vineyard from the highway. Occasionally, you need to get out of your car, tromp the dusty rows and take a closer look.

Grapevines are heroes of mine. In the seventies and eighties they had it pretty rough. Dry farming was the big thing. Grapevines had to push their roots deep through hardpan soil, horde their water like castaways on a desert island, and fight all kinds of diseases like fan leaf virus, Pierce disease, and phylloxera. In those days, vines struggled to get their fruit ripe. 24°Brix was about all the sugar they could manage.

Nowadays, grapevines are pampered like celebrities at a resort spa. Selected clones are matched to specialized rootstocks to best take advantage of various soil types. They are fed fantastic concoctions to encourage vigor, ward off pests and virus, and keep a healthy green glow in their leaves. Their trunks are rubbed free of suckers and their canopies are massaged of extra leaves to allow sunlight through to the grapes. They are encouraged to drink lots of water, and merely have to droop a leaf tip if they wish more.

Grapevines love this star treatment, and they reward their handlers with ripe berries that make luscious, deeply extracted, intense wines full of flavor and texture. If anyone is better at retirement than Jake Lorenzo, it is the modern-day grapevine. They command our respect.

Sure, every now and then, Mother Nature will send some strange weather pattern through Wine Country and make things tough for the grapevines. They'll struggle through harvest season rains trying to get the sugars up in the Chardonnay and Riesling. There may be some mold, but that's what winemakers are for. The grapevines can't do it all. Just as the perfect ripeness approaches for your Merlot, that five-day heat wave will set in and make all the grapes look like raisins. It's not the grapevines' fault. For a grapevine, a heat wave is like a waiter strike. They keep ordering, but they can't get a drink. And when they do, it evaporates before they can drink it. So pick the grapes, get them to the winery and re-hydrate. You'll have better luck next year or the year after that.

Grapevines are stoic. They never get excited. They never get depressed. Rain or shine, there will be fruit on the vine. Once they get going, they will work for you year after year. Grapevines appreciate good hospitality, and they reward the people who pamper them, by giving up their fruit and allowing us to turn it into wine.

If you think about it, wine is *the* beverage of hospitality. I mean what is more hospitable on a warm summer day than a crisp, floral Riesling? What is as playful as the blush of a dry Rosé at a picnic? What defines a celebration more than the joyous pop of a champagne cork? Pinot Noir and beef, Cabernet Sauvignon and lamb, Zinfandel and barbecue all make life more memorable and worth living.

It stands to reason that if grapevines relish hospitality and if the fruit they struggle to ripen produces the beverage of hospitality, then wineries and their representatives must extend that hospitality to their customers. Hospitality needs to be sincere, come from the heart, and must be offered freely without expectation of payment. (This is why Jake Lorenzo can't get used to tasting rooms that charge for samples.)

Ask anyone who's wallowed in it. Jake Lorenzo's hospitality is mighty enjoyable. It gives me pleasure to see people enjoying themselves because of something I like to provide. There are moments in a good evening when the energy syncopates to a perfect rhythm, and I sit quietly charging my spiritual batteries with the wonder of it.

I like to invite chefs over to the house for dinner. Chefs rarely get time off. They love to eat, and people are afraid to cook for them. People worry that chefs will be disappointed with the food you serve them. Jake Lorenzo knows that chefs make the most amenable guests. They are happy with a meal of boiled hot dogs, if you prepare it for them. Give them a cold beer, and they will never forget you.

When I was in the wine business and encountered a group of tourists that had a good attitude and seemed to be having a good time, I'd invite them over to the house for a meal. What a blast. We'd get introduced to strangers, learn about their lives, and share some food and drink. These impromptu meals often served as opening deposits in large accounts of friendship.

Hospitality is a gift of immense proportion, and it has no price. In the face of hospitality, there is only one thing you can do . . . reciprocate. When I am on the road, and someone makes the effort to invite me to their home, I start inviting them to come and visit us before I take that first bite of dessert. On a blistering summer day, when friends invite me over to use their pool, I'm already inviting them over to help press out a load of grapes during the upcoming crush and share some lunch.

Provide hospitality often and over a long period of time, and this reciprocity factor lays out there like buried treasure just waiting to be dug up. We just visited Albuquerque where our friends, Doug and Annie, treated us to a great dinner and a case of different French burgundies followed by magnums of Spanish Priorat, and topped with a grand German Spatlese. Louisiana guests who had been here years ago, had us over to join friends digging into 400 pounds of perfectly cooked crawfish, a pot of jambalaya that could have fed all of the Ninth Ward, and 20 pounds of Boudin so delicious I would have killed two wine writers just to have another piece. New York friends took me to Rao's and then over to the Blue Note to hear a still magnificent Oscar Peterson tickle the ivories.

Grapevines

Hospitality breeds more hospitality. This is a good thing. We live in a world that moves too fast. People hardly have time to eat, let alone take the time to prepare a meal, and sit down with friends to enjoy that meal. We need to make time. It is the legacy of the grapevine to us.

Maybe the grapevine recognizes when we give hospitality to others and reciprocates by giving us great vintages. If that's the case, you better start inviting some people over, because we're due for a great year.

Terroir

March at Jake Lorenzo's house is not a time to relax. First of all it's spring training, and if the baseball players are getting into shape, then this detective might as well get some exercise too. Besides Jakelyn's mother is obsessed with her garden. This means lots of pruning, hauling rocks, shoveling top soil and digging up and moving plants. All this labor puts a serious strain on Jake Lorenzo's back, so I entice friends to come help.

It turns out Dr. Iggy Calamari is a wizard with drip irrigation. He wastes a lot of time testing the soil, reading moisture strips and selecting the proper emitters, but he gets the job done. Jakelyn's mother says that Chuy Palacios has an artistic eye. That means he knows how to prune the roses and she can rely on him for advice about where to move and replant the various trees and flowers to provide the most dramatic effect. That leaves Jake Lorenzo with the donkey work: hauling, lifting and shoveling.

I figure it costs me about a bottle of wine an hour per helper when Iggy and Chuy work in the garden, and they always insist I prepare an elaborate lunch. But Jake Lorenzo has plenty of wine and like we say, "If you don't eat; you die." We were finishing up a very delightful rabbit stew featuring our homemade green olives when Calamari commented

"You've got some nice soil here, Jake."

"Nothing like six years of organic mulch and top soil to make some flowers happy," I replied gently trying to massage the knot out of my hamstring.

Chuy snorted, "See, even the Dr. says 'nice soil.' If it was all your wine geek friends, we'd have to listen to 'terroir' this and 'terroir' that."

I started to explain how important terroir was to fine winemaking, but realized who was at the table with me. Instead I went to the cellar and brought out a Gelsomina Lambrusco. The bubbles in the inky purple liquid freaked them out, but the intense, fruity, bone-dry finish won them over. It was the perfect end to a lovely lunch and they both left before Jakelyn's mom could get them back into the garden.

Once they'd gone, I remained on the porch sipping some homemade Limoncello and pondered terroir. Winemakers emphatically declare the importance of terroir and swear their dedication to protecting the aromas and flavors of a grape's terroir as they go through the winemaking process. They explain terroir as sense of place brought on by the unique interaction of soil, climate and location. This terroir gives a wine its own identity and must be preserved at all costs.

Well, Jake Lorenzo believes in terroir, but I don't agree that every place has a special identity, at least not one that makes special wine. And this detective thinks a lot more goes into terroir than just location, climate and soil. Culture, history and reality all contribute.

For hundreds of years, many have considered French wine the finest in the world. Sure they have great soils, climates that can be sublime and some of the most beautiful rural locations in Europe, but would there be any French wine without the French? The French are among the most provincial of people. What if the world's best terroir for Cabernet Sauvignon is in the Cote d'or? We'll never taste that glorious fruit, because the Burgundians aren't about to let it happen.

Even Charles DeGaulle remarked, "How can you govern a country that has 246 varieties of cheese?" The fierce independence of the French gives their wines a distinctive personality, separates them one region from another, and has lent them a long-term consistency unequalled in other parts of the wine world. Surely that cultural predilection is part of terroir.

From 1920 to 1933 the United States lived under prohibition. Prohibition is not the greatest impetus for fine winemaking. When wine making restarted after prohibition, they used old, contaminated equipment and wooden storage vessels loaded with more microbes than a modern hospital. Just as the industry got going, we went to World War II. Another set-back for the fine wine industry. After the war, it took a while, but California exploded with newly planted vineyards, scientific methodology and stainless steel tanks.

All that technology bred experts and the experts applied their knowledge, not just to winemaking, but to the vineyards as well. Soon we were picking grapes at full physiological maturity. We waited for seeds to turn brown, looked for translucent pulp and waited for flavor development. We let that fruit hang on the vines for a lot longer. Surely that history had an affect on terroir.

Since 1988 when Nicholas Catena imagined a fine wine industry in Argentina, that country has been surging with wonderful wines. Hundreds of hectares are being planted to grapes in the semi-arid foothills of the Andes around the town of Mendoza. Wines are made from exotic varieties like Malbec and Torrontés.

Unlike American vineyards, Argentinian vineyards take nearly a decade to mature.

Very few of the vineyards have wells. For the most part, there is an intricate system of water rights where people share the runoff from the Andes. Water is available on certain days. When it's your turn for water, you can use it or lose it until your next turn. Argentinian grapevines don't get a lot of water. They are tough and hardened with root systems routinely reaching 60 and 70 feet deep. Surely, dealing with the reality of water in Argentina has a major effect on terroir.

Most good winemakers share the same goal. They try to make the best wine from the best fruit they can get. The key is always the vineyard and the vineyard gives the terroir. Looking at the soil, climate and location tells part of the story, but if you want to really understand terroir you need to include the history, culture and real conditions of the people associated with that vineyard.

If you live in a Moslem country with no history of wine consumption, chances are that no one is out looking for vineyard sites. On the other hand, if your family has generations of experience in winemaking, you can't help taking a trip to a foreign country and wondering where the best vineyard site may be.

The attitude of people in an area contributes to the flavor of the wine. If a culture revels in small differences and is stubborn in their desire to retain those differences, then their wines will reflect that. If people are more concerned with the façade, with style and what's hip, then their wines will tend to be flashy and easy to enjoy.

Terroir is deeper than soil. It's more varied than climate. It's a combination of people, culture, tradition and place that allows grapes to grow and express all that is involved in their nurturing.

In Jakelyn's mother's garden terroir is years of hard work, tons of top soil and mulch and loads of loving care. It's also thousands of meals, flower beds used as dump buckets and music wafting from the outside speakers ten hours a day. More than anything it's us and our guests sitting on the porch sipping some wine and appreciating the soaring beauty of a garden in full bloom. Surely, satisfied happiness has some affect on terroir.

Harvest

For the 29th consecutive year, Jake Lorenzo is making wine. When I was younger, less experienced and running a winery, I would get pumped up about harvest. I'd run around like a rookie special teams player looking to get in a good hit. I'd get up in the dark, work all day; get home in the dark and party most of the night. I lived and breathed winemaking. I did everything I could to keep my crew excited and focused. When we were buried by grapes and dug ourselves out; that was exhilarating.

Working harvest was so intense and exciting that I always wanted to share the experience with my friends. I used to invite tourists to help at the winery. I'd invent parties just to get more people involved. For years my parents would come up for crush to help with the homemade wine. We had a pre-crush party, a last day of white grapes party, a harvest party and a last press-load lunch. Then, of course there was tequila night.

It's been 14 years since I last worked crush at a commercial winery, but I've kept my hand in working at home. I set things up so I can do most of the work alone; crushing 500 pound lots, fermenting in 15 gallon containers and ageing in thirty gallon barrels. I use a siphon hose to bottle, put on pressure sensitive labels by hand and put on shrink capsules with a heat gun.

Nowadays, after 29 harvests, Jake Lorenzo finds the whole process relaxing. I know it's going to rain. I know something is going to break. I know there will be some mold. Fermentations will stick, malolactic will be stubborn and barrels will leak. Someone is going to lose their temper and make an ass of himself, but it ain't going to be Jake Lorenzo because I've mellowed with experience. I've learned that no matter how much it rains or how hot it gets, the grapes are still going to come in. When they do, we will turn them into wine.

After all these years, I still get energized by crush. The perfume of clean fermentations stimulates my senses. Punching down tingles my muscles.

Tasting the wine out of the press stimulates my taste buds. The sense of putting finished wine into the barrel always gives me a satisfied sense of accomplishment.

Last week the great jazz duo from New Orleans, Kim Prevost and Bill Solley came to Sonoma to put on a concert. Typically, they were brilliant, challenging themselves and the audience with their passion and virtuosity. One day while they stayed at our house, Jake Lorenzo enlisted them to help with the winemaking.

Initially they thought I was crazy asking them to punch down with their bare arms, but soon they were pressing their open palms through the heated cap into the roiling liquid down below. They became intoxicated with the heady aromas and they marveled at how quickly the heat from the cap was enveloped into the cooler fermenting juice.

When we pressed out a load of Pinot Noir, they laughed at how dirty they got as grapes stuck to their clothes and streams of wine squirted through the press. They took turns cranking and argued good naturedly over who got to break up the cap. They talked about how much fun it would be to involve their three-year-old daughter in this process. They chuckled at the thought of her covered in grapes and stained by wine. They could picture her tiny fingers filling the fermentation locks and placing them on the carboys. After I gave them a taste, they babbled on about how she would love the flavor of freshly settled cold chardonnay juice.

Kim and Bill had lost their home to Hurricane Katrina. Kim's family lost their church (her father was the pastor) and their homes when the lower ninth ward flooded. The whole family is living in a HUD house outside of Houston, Texas. So, it warmed Jake Lorenzo's heart to see Kim and Bill laughing and joking and hugging one another. This couple had suffered so much, but the process and magic of making wine had given them enough joy to make them laugh.

Not only that, but they were already planning on bringing their daughter Sofia out next year so she could participate in harvest. It reminded me of all the years Jakelyn helped with crush. Later, our son-in-law and the grandbabies pitched in. I remember Kieran and Kerrissa Toovey working at the press after their father had been murdered, and we made vintage after vintage from the grapes he had planted in their back yard.

Winemaking teaches us that there are cycles. The vines bud, set fruit, ripen and eventually go dormant. The wine ferments, ages and gets drunk. One year flows into the next. We learn that we must do the work when it is required, that we must work in the face of exhaustion and we must strive for excellence. We learn there will be good vintages and poorer vintages, but no matter the calamity, there will always be another harvest.

Harvest and winemaking have become so much a part of Jake Lorenzo's life that I sometimes forget the thrill and magic it provides for others. Friends still call in harvest season to find out when they can come to the house and help. People I met more than 20 years ago still telephone to find out about the crush, never failing to say they hope they can come out one more time to operate my press. Kids grow up, go to college and begin careers, but they always mention the time they helped Uncle Jake make wine.

In modern America there is very little opportunity to commune with our food source. Our meat is cut and wrapped in plastic packages. Our fish sits on ice devoid of bones and scales already cut into filets. Our produce comes pre-washed in plastic bags. Hell, most people don't even do their own cooking anymore. In a world where we are further removing ourselves from the source, real magic is critical.

Harry Houdini was a magician, but he didn't make magic. It was all illusion. Real magic feeds the soul. Winemaking is real magic. Taking grapes from the vine and turning the juice into wine is as magical as life gets. There's so much magic in making wine that the end product actually makes you high. But the real magic is in the making. Getting high is the illusion of magic.

Kim Prevost and Bill Solley are magicians. The two of them take the gifts of voice and talent to make some of the most soul-stirring, sensuous jazz music being made these days. It's the making of the music that is the magic.

After the concert, we all go back to Jake Lorenzo's house. We have known each other for more than six years and have been through a lot together. Jakelyn's mom opens some wine and we sit and talk late into the night. Kim likes white wine. At my house this is a very good thing. It leaves more red wine for the rest of us. Is that magic? I don't think so, but next year when Kim and Bill return with their daughter for harvest and they open a bottle of the wine that they helped make; that will be a magic evening. It's one night I don't plan on missing.

Wine Appreciation 101

W ho decided that punching down grapes was a good thing?

Jake Lorenzo would like to find that bastard and drown him in a fermenting vat of rosé. It feels like I've been punching down tanks since bud break. Every part of my body hurts. My neck won't turn anymore. My shoulders are sore. My abs are like rippled steel, and if it wasn't for the fact that I insist on eating and drinking enough for two people, everyone would be telling me what great shape I'm in. Jake Lorenzo's not looking to get into shape. I'm looking to be done. I'm sick of driving to the winery three or four times a day to punch down. Let's get this stuff fermented, pressed and into the barrels.

Punching down is repetitive and it's boring, but it gives one pause for contemplation. About a month ago Marcelo Hernandez picked his wonderful Carneros Merlot for Relentless Vineyards. I was out in the vineyard as his family arrived to do the picking. I noticed two teenaged boys in the group and asked Marcelo who they were. "Those are some of my grandkids, Jake. They were raised picking Grandpa's grapes and they don't like to miss it."

I surveyed the tiny two-acre vineyard. Marcelo's sons and daughters and grandchildren were all wielding knives and picking grapes. They sorted out the leaves and moved from row to row laughing and conversing. Boxes of grapes were dumped into gondolas and loaded onto the truck. Three generations of Hernandezes worked side by side helping Marcelo get in the harvest, and they had been doing it for their entire lives.

Marcelo Hernandez first came to Sonoma in 1966. He got a job with Charlie Spumer who taught him all about grapes. Five years later he started working for Jim Bundschu and he brought his wife and eight kids up to

Sonoma from Mexico. He worked for Bundschu for 30 years caring for the vineyards, growing the grapes that made the winery famous.

Saving his money, Marcelo bought a three-acre parcel on Burndale Road in the Sonoma Carneros. He and his sons built a house on the property, and then on the rest of the lot, he planted Merlot grapes. Marcelo has over 30 years of experience in the wine business managing over 300 acres of prime Sonoma Valley grapes, but the 1,410 vines planted on his property are something special. He personally put up the plant stakes, ran the wire, and placed the irrigation hoses. He has personally planted, nurtured and pruned every single vine.

Marcelo is a strong, quiet man. He is the hardest working man Jake Lorenzo has ever met. I have seen him on his back, in the mud, working on a broken tractor. I've seen him working for three days straight with no sleep. I've seen him deal with a crew of 24 diverse individuals, without ever once demeaning them or showing them a lack of respect. I've seen him raise and marry off each of his eight children. I've seen him laugh and cry and get old, but I've never seen Marcelo drink wine.

Oh, he'll taste a glass now and then, and he likes really sweet late harvest wines, but basically he doesn't drink wine. For the most part neither do his kids. This family whose every autumn has revolved around the grape harvest does not partake of the fruit of their labor.

This got Jake Lorenzo to thinking as I was punching down grapes feeling the sting in my muscles and trying to get my stiff neck to turn and look at the crew working at the winery. These days a large percentage of the cellar rat population is decidedly Mexicano. I know dozens of Mexicanos who have worked at wineries for years. They manage harvest and run the crusher, press, and barrel down. They filter, they rack and they bottle. They understand chemical reactions, how to fix leaky barrels and how to measure the amount of oxygen in a wine, but they don't drink the wine.

It's amazing to me that in many cases the very people dedicated to making this magical elixir that we call wine don't drink it themselves. They never experience the charms of a crisp, dry Gewürztraminer. They remain unmoved by the alluring beauty of a great Pinot Noir and they are unimpressed by a bold, luscious Cabernet. They do the work with enough pride and expertise to produce some of the finest wines the world has to offer, but they don't partake in the sweetly juiced pleasures of a three hour lunch.

It wasn't like that in the seventies and eighties. Cellar rats in the good old days drank beer during the harvest, but at night and the rest of the year it was all about the wine. We would work all week and then go to the other wineries on the weekends so we could taste the competition. We would buy huge amounts of wine from our own wineries (using our 50% discount) and then trade as much as we could to see what the neighbors were doing. Cellar rats would join tasting groups and go to public tastings. We'd drink wine every night with dinner.

We learned differences between barrel fermented and tank fermented Chardonnay. We tasted Sauvignon Blancs from France, New Zealand and South Africa. We discovered Cotes du Rhone, Rioja, Malbec from Argentina and Port from the Douro. We swooned over Burgundy, were provoked by Brunello and lit up over Champagne. If someone made it from grapes and put it into a bottle, then we wanted to drink it.

We cellar rats saw ourselves as the true winemakers, the valid keepers of the flame. We knew how to get the magic into the bottle, and once opened and in our glass, that wine would unleash its magic on our souls.

Making wine is hard work. Hooking up hoses on a cold winter morning in a winery filled with ice-covered tanks hurts. Crushing grapes wearing rubber boots and walking on cement for twelve hours a day for the eight weeks of harvest is not for the weak at heart. Standing on the bottling line day after day is tedious and mind-numbing. How much harder must it be for the worker who doesn't enjoy taking a bottle off the line home for dinner?

Some critics complain that wines are starting to taste the same. They complain about too much alcohol or too much fruit or not enough finesse. They decry the competition to see who can charge the most for a bottle, build the grandest shrine and score the most points.

Jake Lorenzo just wishes the people who make the wines could enjoy what they have wrought.

No cellar rat expects to get rich on the job, but we should at least be able to drink like royalty. If the history and traditions of wine are foreign to our Mexicano cellar rats, then it behooves us to educate them. I'm not talking about classrooms and lectures, but palpable history. Tell them about the

Chinese who worked in the fledgling wine business after building the railroads and ending up in California without other work. Show them the rich history in Europe and explain how long a history it is. Take them to Baja California so they can see the burgeoning Mexican wine industry.

More than anything, we need to set up informal tasting situations. They don't need to try to learn vocabulary and descriptors or to memorize regions and varieties. They need to experience the pleasure a good dry Gewürztraminer brings to a well-made *albondigas* soup. Expose them to the charms of a Zinfandel with *cabrito*. Take them out to a local restaurant for a three-hour lunch where they match all kinds of wine with different dishes. Have them delight in wine-food pairings and have them experience the warm glow of several bottles with friends. Let them see that it's the wine that makes them laugh and talk and joke about work and life. And be sure to remind them that this is the product of their labor, that they have created this magical potion that feeds the soul.

Making wine is hard dirty work. All of us who make it should reap the special rewards it offers. When workers understand the power of the elixir in the bottle, they are driven to enhance it and to make it better. That would be a benefit for all of us.

Tell Me a Story

"It's all about what's in the bottle," Chuy argued. "I don't care what happened in the vineyard, whether or not it rained in the middle of harvest of if the winemaker had a fight with his wife the day before the grapes were crushed. I pull the cork, taste the wine and decide whether I like it or not."

"You sound like a wine critic," countered Jake Lorenzo. "Are you going to start rating the wines on a 100 point system? Your taste is different from everyone else's. Who cares what you think? Why is it important?"

"I care about what I think," Chuy said, "and it's important because I'm the one buying the bottle."

Jake Lorenzo, private eye, runs up against this attitude often. In fact, to a certain extent, I can agree with the logic behind it. Each and every bottle of wine has a responsibility to provide enjoyment and pleasure to the ultimate consumer. But there are millions and millions of bottles of wine sitting on the shelves waiting for us to make a purchase. Most of us don't have the time and commitment to taste all of these wines and decide what we like the best. We certainly don't have the money to taste them all, so we rely on critics to help us make our choices.

It's a bit like going to the horse races and reading over the handicapper's list. We hear about the past history of the horse, what kind of weights they carry, who sired them, who's riding them, etc. Even though most of us know nothing about horse racing, we use this information to make our bets, as if we know how to analyze the information. Then most of the time, we lose our money. It's similar to buying a bottle of wine that scores 95 from some critic and taking it home only to find that it is over-ripe, over-extracted and over-oaked with enough alcohol to make you think about attending an AA meeting when you finish it.

People will bet horses because they have their kid's name or because they like the jockey's colors or the number of the horse. I've been to the races with people who always bet the grey horse. All of them usually lose their money. It's the same as people who buy a bottle of wine because they like the cute animal on the label or the shape of the bottle.

Jake Lorenzo knows a lot of winemakers. They come to my house because I know how to cook and I will feed them. During a multi-course meal with several bottles of wine, these winemakers loosen up. They tell stories. They talk about the difference between their best wines and the best job of winemaking they have done. I find these stories intriguing.

Way back in 1989 one winemaker talked about how the interminable rain caused his Zinfandel to rot. There was too much rot to cut out and the winery owner grew the grapes so the winemaker had to take them. When the picked grapes were dumped into the hopper a cloud of mold spores filled the air and blotted out the sun much like all the smoke from the California fires did last month. But he worked on that wine. He cared for it. By the time it went into bottle, it had a brambly, peppery character that he and everyone who tasted the wine loved. He told me it was a great job of winemaking or just dumb luck. He was never sure of which.

Another winemaker regaled us about a 1980 Zinfandel that came in at 25° Brix. He laughed as he explained that most winemakers were trying to get grapes between 22 and 23.5° Brix in those days. The next day he checked the tank and it read 27° Brix. He went ahead and fermented the grapes, massaged the temperature, aerated the must and finally got the wine dry. He said it had a terrific jammy character with a long berry flavor and no discernable high alcohol on the finish. It aged great for over 20 years.

In 2003, this detective had a batch of Napa Cabernet stick at 13°Balling. (I should have known better than to try fermenting Napa grapes in *my* garage.) I had to re-inoculate, build the yeast bit by bit, drag the fermenters out into the sun to warm them daily, but after six weeks I finally got the stuff to go dry. Is it the best wine I've ever made? No, but it was some of the best winemaking I've ever done.

Jake Lorenzo thinks that wineries and winemakers are missing a marketing bonanza. While most consumers seem to look for the safest bet, others of us are looking for the good story. Instead of writing some generic drivel about how great the vineyard is and how balanced the wine is, how about writing that the rain wreaked havoc, but the winemaker saved the day? I'd like to try that wine.

Tell me that the winemaker thinks a bottle of wine represents some of the greatest winemaking he's ever done and I'll look for that bottle until I find it, even if it's a Rosé. Tell me a bottle comes from the last vintage of a particular vineyard because the grapes have been ripped out for a housing tract and Jake Lorenzo will search out that last gasp of a vineyard, just to see what the world will miss. Explain that the winemaker thought California Sangiovese was too acidic to make a stand-alone varietal, but thought it would be the perfect thing to blend into low acid Tempranillo and I'd be on it like a $5 Ribiero del Duero.

I know that grapes are the key ingredient for making wine. Terroir is critical. Brix, pH and total acidity are measures sometimes used by winemakers to evaluate their produce. Oak comes from different forests with tighter or wider grains and winemakers choose from a variety of toast levels, but Jake Lorenzo loves a good story.

Tell me something interesting about the people making a particular bottle and I want to buy it. Regale me about how the crusher broke when the grapes for that bottle arrived, and I want to taste what the crew did to overcome it. Show me a diagram of how the fires came to the edge of a vineyard, and I'll try that vintage to see if I can taste the smoke. Explain how you rid your organic vineyard of leafhoppers and I may get concerned about health issues in winemaking.

The point I'm trying to make is that there are hundreds of reasons to buy a bottle of wine. As far as Jake Lorenzo is concerned, wine ratings are the least interesting. I like personal stories, challenges met and accomplished, harrowing tales of near misses turned into successes. I can enjoy a good, well made wine produced under trying conditions as much as a delicious wine made in a perfect vintage.

Wineries spend a lot of time focusing on their images. Often maintaining those images involves elaborate semi-fictitious stories. Wineries should let their consumers know the truth. The uncontestable difficulty of making fine wine year after year precludes easy, great vintages year after year. Tell the very human story of how you overcame the difficulties and consumers will embrace your wines. The truth shall set you free.

Variety Is The Spice of Life

Even Mother Nature can't make everyone in her kingdom happy. Our magnolia tree loved the recent heat wave, putting out huge, glorious white blooms. The tomato plants grew like crazy, finally starting to color and ripen their fruit. On the other hand, the heat baked into the ground and reflected up onto the plants in Jakelyn's mother's garden. Leaves on the Green Goddess lilies turned brown. Gladiola buds shriveled before they could bloom. The broad-leafed squash plants wilted like tired marathon runners quitting miles before the finish of a race.

Nobody likes everything. What some people think is terrific, other people hate. Jake Lorenzo likes going barefoot, wearing baseball caps and drinking ice cold beer on a hot afternoon. I like loud, colorful shirts, but dependable unassuming cars. I like three-hour lunches, afternoons on boats and reading a good book with my stereo cranked up. I don't get bungie-cord jumping, burritos with rice or "mild" hot sauce.

I'm not one of those people who think you should like what I like, and I'm certainly not going to try to convince you that I am the final arbiter of taste. I like variety in my life. It makes things interesting. How dull would it be if the only ice cream was Rocky Road?" What if all the restaurants were exactly like the French Laundry? If it was sunny with blue skies and 75 degree temperatures *every day*, I'd go crazy (or wonder how I ended up in San Diego.)

Jake Lorenzo thinks the key to life is variety and it's one of the reasons I like wine so much. Every encounter with a bottle of wine is an adventure. It involves making a choice and taking a chance. First off, you've got to pick a color. Traditionally in table wine, your choices are white, red or pink. (I've seen plenty of wines that were brown, but other than some aged sweet wines, I generally steer clear of the color brown in table wine.)

When it comes to colors I'll admit that pink wine is not my favorite. I try them on hot summer days. They rarely have the crisp fruitiness of white wine, nor do they have the complexity of red wines. They are served cold, which is good and they can be refreshing as a delightful accompaniment to a light lunch. I do like sparkling wines made from red grapes and they are light pink or rose colored. The acidity is high and the bubbles are festive and the pink plays well in a flute glass.

Jake Lorenzo prefers red wine over white wine but I love a spicy, dry Gewürztraminer, or a crisp, low-alcohol Riesling. A cold, tangy Torrontes works well with lots of different foods and I'll drink a Chardonnay if it's not too oaky and it has some acidity along with the richness. White wines exude a fruity freshness that titillates the taste buds, that's why people like them; it's also why I prefer red wines.

With white wines, that first taste is the best one, because they are constructed to focus on the fruit. Most white wines avoid oak and they have little tannin. The fruit flavor explodes in your mouth. It sends refreshing shivers down to your soul, but then the alcohol slowly dulls your taste buds. As your taste buds tire, the explosions of fruit diminish and that first rush of flavor is just a memory. Since sheer fruitiness is carrying the bulk of taste, once that fruitiness begins to dull, so does the wine. The wine may be good, but it never lives up to that first, great blast of flavor.

Red wines are different. Fermenting with the skins, barrel ageing, slow oxygenation through racking or micro-ox all create complex compounds of flavor. The first sip of red wine may reveal fruitiness or vanilla from the oak, but in a good red wine each subsequent sip reveals another layer of flavor. With red wine, the last sip is the best and the drinker comes to appreciate all of the various complexities of aroma and flavor.

Once you pick a color, and Jake Lorenzo picks red, then you must choose a variety. The simple charms of a lush Merlot can please the palate. Merlot is the Alex Rodriguez of wine. It's a great star that can shine on its own or work as part of a team, but in either case the locals boo whenever it steps up to the plate.

Cabernet Sauvignon is king and for a good reason. Good Cabernets are extracted and rich with a strong tannic backbone promising years of ageing potential. They have a depth of complexity that expresses itself over time, both in the bottle and in the glass. A classically good Cabernet changes so much in the glass that it's like opening two or three different bottles of wine.

Zinfandel has that brash, in-your-face, "what you see is what you get" thing going for it. It is to the wine world what Americans are to foreigners. It can be little hot…so what? The berry, jammy goodness of Zinfandel can brighten any table and with time hints of pepper complex the flavors especially when paired with barbecue or grilled lamb.

Syrah is a favorite of Jake Lorenzo. Budget has a lot to do with it. Faced with shopping in a wine shop, Jake always seems to migrate toward the Cotes du Rhone section. The purple color of Syrah promises depth and its combination of spice, pepper and ripe fruit character make it interesting, even when it is young. The big tannic structure challenges and makes it eager to work in tandem with other grapes.

Malbec from Argentina, Grenache and Mouvedre from Spain, Sangiovese from Italy. I love them all for different reasons. I choose different varieties as often as I can, but in the end my favorite varietal is Pinot Noir. First of all, Pinot Noir is hard to make. It prefers cool weather and hillsides with chalky soil. It prefers to be treated gently and with respect. In the cellar, it behaves differently from year to year, thus resisting formulaic winemaking. In the bottle it can go through a dumb phase tricking some into drinking it too soon, but giving huge rewards to those with patience.

Good Pinot Noir has a delicate elegance and a luscious succulence that can transport you to another place. It is not the stop-traffic beauty of bombshell Jessica Alba or thick-lipped Angelina Jolie, but more the classic elegance of Catherine Denueve or Isabella Rosselini. The charms of Pinot Noir are subtle and require patience. Pinot Noir rewards those with astute palates and experience. Great aged Pinot Noir provides the most ethereal wine drinking pleasure known to this detective.

Wine is not the only thing that provides us with loads of variety. There are thousands of different cheeses, hundreds of good whiskies and an infinite number of gorgeous flowers. But whiskey doesn't change in the bottle, flowers bloom and die in a few days, cheese develops until it stinks so bad that turkey buzzards circle your house looking for dead bodies.

Wine gives us variety and longevity. It develops and changes in the bottle, allowing us to revel in its various stages of development. A mature, well-made red wine will reveal its entire life over the course of one glass. You can taste the fruitiness of youth and the recklessness of adolescence. You can wallow in textured maturity and be saddened by the hints of old age.

Wine is living history in a glass, and it makes us high. That is a gift of the highest order. So pick a color. Pick a variety. Then sit back and enjoy the ride.

Jake's On The Case

Lean with a comfortable elegance, she sat in the chair oozing athletic grace. She slid her finger down the sweating glass of iced tea and turned her blue eyes my way. She smiled, the kind of smile that could make a man empty his savings account and buy two one-way tickets to Provence. Her voice had the rich huskiness of a well aged Cabernet, "As I said, Mr. Lorenzo, we have worked very hard to earn a reputation as one of the finest wineries in the world. I cannot afford to have that reputation tarnished or reduced in any way."

"Why me?" I asked. "There are plenty of private eyes to pick from."

"I like to stay local," she sighed, her voice as hot as a Pinot Noir fermentation, "and you come very highly recommended."

Everyone likes to be stroked, but Jake Lorenzo is no one's lap dog. "Let me get this straight," I said. "You're convinced someone is sabotaging your wine, but there's no one who has any reason to do so. Your ex-husband and you are hunky dory, your employees love working for you and finances are no problem. You can think of absolutely no one who wants to do you or your winery harm."

She nodded in agreement and then seductively used her left hand to brush the hair from her eyes. I forced myself to concentrate. "How are they sabotaging your wine?" I asked.

"I'm not exactly sure, she said wrinkling her nose in the most adorable yet adult way, "but to be frank it stinks." She fixed those baby blue eyes on me one more time. "My wine stinks Mr. Lorenzo. Somebody is trying to ruin me. I need you to find out who it is and stop them."

Starting an investigation is a lot like finding out what's wrong when something breaks on a bottling line. Start with the obvious. Is the machine plugged in? Have you blown a fuse or flipped a breaker? Only after checking the obvious should you look into more complex causes, like maybe something's actually broken.

This case was easy: the butler did it … except she didn't have a butler. That left the ex-husband and the employees. I went to the winery to check out the help, figuring I had a better chance of tasting some wine there than at the ex-husband's.

The stunning landscaping featured dozens of different flowers, striking variegated leaves and unique ground covers. The vineyard fanned out across a south-facing hill filling about 12 acres with Sauvignon Blanc, Pinot Noir and God bless her, Tempranillo. The vineyards were well tended with crop that looked like two to three tons per acre. Jake Lorenzo was impressed.

The winery was pretty without being ostentatious. Clean without being anal. The thirty-something winemaker went by the name of Ferm. "My parents loved wine," he explained, "So they named me Fermentation. I was sort of predestined to get into this business."

Name aside, Ferm seemed OK. Fairly new to the business with only four years experience, he confirmed that everyone got along with the boss and he agreed someone was sabotaging the wine. "Actually," Ferm said, "They're only messing up the white wine. So far they haven't gone after the reds."

Now, there was a clue that Jake Lorenzo could understand. Someone sabotaging white wine only. I saw my chance and I took it. "We better taste the wines. Let's start with the reds and then I'll try that white." Ferm led me to the comfortable tasting room. The Pinot Noir was silky and full of earthy, strawberry fruit without being so high in alcohol that it finished like a Zin. It showed balanced oak and a subtle complexity. I complemented Ferm on a wine that actually tasted like Pinot Noir.

Ferm pulled the cork on the Tempranillo. Huge, with a deep purple color and complex, ripe berry fruit, it had a sumptuous mouth filling character and a nicely astringent tannic finish. "Ribero del Duero in California," I praised.

"It's the vineyards," Ferm said humbly. Anyone could make great wine with these grapes even a moke like me with no formal training"

He pulled the Sauvignon Blanc bottle and I commented on the screw cap closure. "Marketing department," Ferm sneered. "I wouldn't let them go near my reds, but I had to compromise somewhere. That's the mystery. There's no way to tamper with these bottles once they're sealed. I'm very careful about applying the correct torque specs to ensure the seal and I insist on checking it every 10 to 15 minutes. When this wine went into the bottle it was fresh, crisp, aromatic and full of citrus, bell pepper, mineral flavors." He shook his head with disgust as he unscrewed the cap and poured me a glass. "Look what's happened."

I sniffed at the wine. It stunk. Where once there might have been citrus and bell pepper, now I got eggy, cat piss aromas. I tasted the wine and got a nasty, cabbage taste. I asked for a couple more sample bottles, thanked Ferm for his time and decided I might not have to talk to the ex-husband or check the financials.

Instead I took off for Dr. Iggy Calamari's lab. I might have solved the case, but I wanted the good doctor to confirm some stuff for me. Iggy bent over a microscope checking out cells. "These, Mr. Detective, could be the answer to Alzheimer's. If I can just figure a way to remove this funky plaque that builds up on the brain cells, we may not have to lose our faculties as we age."

Fortunately, I hadn't started to lose my faculties yet and I was focused. "Calamari," I said as I unscrewed the cap on a bottle of Sauvignon Blanc, "I think I've solved a case but I need some corroboration. This stuff stinks, and the winery thinks they're being sabotaged, but I think it's some of that reduction I've been reading about." I go on to give him the facts in the case, leaving out a description of the owner, because Calamari hates when I have beautiful clients.

Iggy smells the wine, wrinkles his nose and refuses to taste it. "Well, I'm not the detective, but as a meager scientist I must point out that the wine is bottled under screw cap, it smells like rotten eggs and it's made by a fairly inexperienced winemaker, so it's elementary my dear Mr. Lorenzo." Calamari went on to explain that reduction is not a description of something you smell. Sulfur aromas and flavors occur because the wine is in a "reductive state." Earlier presence of sulfur compounds usually formed during fermentation and reductive winemaking techniques like using inert gas, maintaining high levels of SO_2 and using closures that limit egress of oxygen can contribute to the sulfur aromas after bottling.

"It's kind of like dry rot in a house," he explains, "You can't see it, but if you don't fix it the entire house can collapse."

"How do you fix it in wine?" I asked.

"It's quite simple really. You perform a copper sulfate fining, the sooner the better. In most cases that should pretty much alleviate the problem." Calamari explained in a lot more detail and gave me some 1% copper sulfate solution to take to Ferm along with instructions on how and when to use it.

I headed back to the winery. The case was solved, and I was hoping for a couple cases of red wine as a bonus.

Peace On Earth

The Mendocino Coast is always beautiful, but today is extraordinary. The view fills with blue sky, turquoise water and waves crashing into white foam on the black rocks. The tide pools brim with anemones, hermit crabs and star fish. Harbor seals lounge on the rocks. Seagulls hop around looking for food. Pelicans fly in single-file lines. This warm, sunny fall day is spectacular, and a perfect way to recover from a long, stuttering harvest season.

As tranquil as the ocean appears, this detective knows better. Killer waves lurk out in the ocean eager to loom up out of nowhere and sweep unsuspecting tourists out to sea. More than once Jake Lorenzo has been smashed into rocks while hunting abalone, left gasping for breath and fighting to get to the surface. In the spring, when the harbor seal pups are learning to swim, sharks cruise malignantly hoping for a tasty meal.

The Mendocino Coast may appear tranquil, but there is a fierce, untamed quality to life on the cliffs and in the forests and in the ocean. It can get cold and foggy and so windy that the chill slices through the flesh all the way to your bone marrow. A lovely day of mushroom hunting can easily send a novice to the emergency room or even the morgue. A leisurely drive through the hills and a wrong turn can direct a tourist to an armed confrontation with a pot farmer somewhere near Competche.

Out of necessity, the people of Mendocino remain ferocious with a certain feral quality. They love to argue and will take any side in a debate. Tell them they can't do something and they will immediately start to try. Abridge any one of their rights they will fight tooth and nail to reacquire them. There are more beards than barbers and more joints than cigarettes. The county attracts rugged individualists, radical religious cults, confrontational lesbian groups and militant vegans.

So Jake Lorenzo, private eye, was stunned to discover that Mendocino has uncovered the secret to peace on earth.

It started with my reading a little blurb in a local weekly announcing a wine tasting at the rustic, but luxurious Stanford Inn by the Sea. Ten Mendocino wineries were pouring their Coro wines. Jake Lorenzo wasn't exactly sure what Coro wines were, but I'd heard about them. Since I'm a detective; I figured I should investigate. Entering the tasting I realized that Coro wines were pretty much a secret. My motley group included Chuy and his date, Dr. Iggy Calamari, Captain Jon, Jakelyn's mother and myself. We accounted for half of the attendees.

Jake Lorenzo knows that one thing winemakers hate is having to attend a tasting when nobody comes, especially after a long harvest while they still have wines cooking in fermenters. So, I was pleasantly surprised to see all the winemakers in good spirits, sipping each other's wines and swapping crush stories. It turns out Coro wines are pretty good and participating winemakers get very cool black shirts with the Coro logo on the pocket.

According to their press kit, "Coro Mendocino is a collaborative effort by Mendocino winemakers to create a class of distinctive wines that showcase the rich heritage and unique characteristics of Mendocino County." Only Mendocino fruit can be used and Zinfandel must be the primary varietal comprising somewhere between 40 to 70 percent of the blend. Blending varieties are limited to Syrah, Petite Sirah, Carignane, Sangiovese, Grenache, Dolcetto, Charbono, Barbera and Primitivo.

Not only are the varietals for the blend restricted, but the methods of winemaking are regulated including the finished alcohol, pH and TA. Wines must be barrel aged for a minimum of one-and-a-half years and then bottled for a minimum of at least one year before release. Participating wineries must submit their blends to a judging panel for a series of blind tastings. Only when the blends meet the approval of the panel of judges can the wine be considered Coro Mendocino. All of the Coro Mendocino wines share a uniform bottle, label and the trademarked logo. Each winery then personalizes the group label for its own special bottling.

Jake Lorenzo loved the whole idea of Coro Mendocino. None of this French snobby Bordeaux blend. Hell no. The craggy, individualistic winemakers of Mendocino pegged the whole venture on Zinfandel,

California's own unique grape. Then they decided to tweak the hell out of it. Brutocao Cellars adds Barbera, Syrah, and Dolcetto. Greg Graziano includes Petite Sirah, Barbera, Sangiovese, Carignane and Dolcetto. This is inspired madness, but madness never-the-less. If you doubt that, you need to see the Coro tattoos being sported by Casey Hartlip and Fred Nickel.

Each wine is incredibly and indelibly different from the others. All share a rugged, independent spirit loaded with mountain fruit flavors. Some of the blends seem to make sense in a winemaking tradition. Others, just as delicious, come out of left field to open new horizons and thought patterns for interested vintners.

I know that getting two winemakers to agree on anything is as likely to happen as seeing George Bush wielding hammers alongside Jimmy Carter in a Habitat for Humanity home in New Orleans East. Winemakers argue over bottle closures, organic farming, native yeast, types of oak and affects of music on the taste of a glass of wine. Winemakers can't figure out how to divide a $30 check at the Burrito Palace. How did they come up with Coro Mendocino?

Winemakers have egos, big egos. It goes with the job. These Mendocino vintners have to submit their prized wines in brown bags and let other winemakers criticize the hell out of them. If the group says a particular wine doesn't make the grade, then "You're outta here, and take your ego with you."

Coro Mendocino understands creative compromise. Not only did they put their wines, egos and reputations on the line; they democratically devised a uniform bottle and label that still allows individual wineries to personalize the package. That's brilliant.

Call Condoleeza Rice and tell her to get her butt on a plane to Mendocino. She can learn something about diplomacy from these crusty Mendocino winemakers. Keep all those State department sycophants in their offices. Send these blue-jeaned, Mendocino vintners to the mid-East.

I figure it will take them less than a month. The war in Iraq will be over. Iran will stop their nuclear research. The Palestinians and Israelis will resume peace talks and Moslems will come to love red wine from Mendocino. They can do it. Jake Lorenzo has seen them work. World Peace will be ours.

Then just for laughs, I'd like to watch a video of Condoleeza Rice trying to sell an oak barrel to John Parducci. There's shock and awe for you.

On The Passing
of Dreams

In the late 1960s, the first California varietal wines to grace this detective's palate came from the new Robert Mondavi Winery in Oakville. I had no idea where Oakville was, since I was often mired in my daily commute from Santa Monica to East Los Angeles where I was teaching Hispanic kids to read in English. Teaching got me into drinking and drinking led me to the wine business.

By 1977, Jake Lorenzo had moved, with his family in tow, to California Wine Country. It was certainly one of the best life decisions I have ever made. In my 30 years working in the wine business, I never passed an evening with Robert Mondavi. I shook his hand a couple of times, had a couple of superficial conversations and in the very early days spent many a delightful evening listening to the superb music at his summer concerts.

He was a big man, tall with a booming voice and an enthusiasm that matched, but more than anything Mondavi was a salesman and a dreamer. His dream was to sell a pile of California wine and his pitch was to take on the established, great wines of the world and challenge them "mano a mano" with his upstart varietals.

Robert Mondavi would march into the greatest restaurants in the world. He would plunk his bottles down on the table, order some of the famous First Growths off the list and insist that his guests taste the wines side by side, knowing that just having his bottles on the same table as the great wines of France lent them an air of legitimacy. He would smile his snake-oil grin and concede, "We're not there yet, but someday soon our California wines will be as good as theirs." Then he would pay the bill, tip large and move to the next grand restaurant to repeat the show.

Mondavi was our ambassador to the wine world. He pushed his winemakers to compete with the finest wines of the world because he knew that was where the money was. He was imaginative, insistent, clever and decidedly American in his brash, trash-talking challenge of the established icons of wine. His surprising legacy is that he not only convinced the French and Europeans that California could compete with them; he convinced us that our wine was as good as theirs.

Every California winemaker will be forever indebted to Robert Mondavi because he took the high road in trying to sell his upstart wines, and that high road was to dedicate his efforts to quality.

Mondavi's passing reminds me of others who have left us, others far less famous but not necessarily less important. Next year will be the 20th anniversary of Tracy Toovey's death. Tracy exemplified the enthusiasm, dedication and sense of wonder that comprised the wine industry in the 70s and 80s. Tracy worked as the cellar master at Grand Cru Winery. The hours were long and the work was very difficult. Pay was not much higher than minimum wage.

Tracy was gentle and kind, but he was fiercely determined to make fine wine and he took immense pride when his attempts succeeded. Tracy, like most of us in those days, lived and breathed winemaking. We hadn't come from families with wine history and we were eager to make up for lost time. We all held wine tastings, traded wine and shared any wines we could find from other countries. A chance to taste some of the great wines from France or Italy would see a whole group of us piled into a car going to San Francisco, even if it meant having to work at the winery over the weekend to make up for lost time.

When Tracy got married, the ceremony was held at Grand Cru Winery. Lance Cutler performed the nuptials. Mark Stupich, Jeff McBride and Ray Kaufman all sang in the choir. The guests made up a who's who of working winemakers and cellar rats and the sheer amount of wine consumed would have made Robert Mondavi confident about the success of California varietals in the future.

Over the next few years Tracy and his wife had two kids and bought a tiny house in Glen Ellen. Most evenings and weekends he would work on the house adding on bedrooms or a dining room or installing new handmade kitchen cabinets. He planted some vines in his backyard and made wine from those grapes. Tracy worked at a job he loved, passed his time with a family that he worshipped and spent time exploring hobbies and interests that intrigued him.

In 1989 Tracy Toovey, like the rest of us, had been in the wine business for more than 10 years. We had seen demand for our wines grow and grow. We had been through one ill-financed expansion after another. We had learned our lessons about cold stability, heat stability, malolactic fermentations and brettanomyces infection. We reveled in harvest, groaned on the bottling lines and enthusiastically shared each new bottling with our contemporaries as soon as they were bottled. Life was good.

Then, for Tracy Toovey, life was over. Tracy was murdered on April 14th, 1989 at the winery by Ruben Salcido who was reportedly drunk and coked up. Salcido ended up killing seven people including his wife and two of his children.

For Grand Cru Winery, the aftermath was not their finest hour. They refused to even pay for health insurance for the surviving Toovey family. Cellar rats, vineyard workers and other winery workers in Sonoma Valley stepped into the breach. We signed petitions donating one hour's pay each year so that Tracy's family would have continued health care.

The harvest of 1989 was one of the rainiest on record. It was as if the sorrow over Tracy's death had opened up the tear ducts in the sky and it couldn't stop crying. The mud was so deep in the vineyards that it would suck the boots right off your feet. Whole blocks of Chardonnay grapes rotted to nothing on the vines.

In 1989 most of us in the wine business were young, strong, passionate and in love with our jobs and our lives. To lose Tracy, someone our own age, someone with a family like ours, someone who shared our aspirations, was a devastating blow. It made us think. It made me think about life, family and what is truly important.

Robert Mondavi had a dream, and he will be remembered in history books for achieving that dream and creating the California wine industry as we know it. Jake Lorenzo says that Mondavi never would have achieved that dream were it not for the likes of Tracy Toovey. It was the dedication and enthusiasm that hundreds of workers like Tracy brought to the wine industry that gave it the extraordinary spirit that lifted it into the 21st century.

Tracy Toovey had a dream. He never got to see it through. But he changed Jake Lorenzo's life, and without your knowing it, he changed yours too. Robert Mondavi can have the history books. Tracy has this detective's heart. I hope you are lucky enough to have memories of him tucked into yours as well.

Big Sister and
the Grandbaby

The new grandbaby is rooting though a basket removing each and every toy. Once the toy basket empties, she climbs into the box, giggling, making train noises. After a bit she exclaims, "Uh, oh," climbs out of the box and puts each of the toys back in. She gnaws on a pretzel, drinks some milk from a sippy-cup, and then focuses on emptying the basket again.

She entertains herself with the toys and basket until Big Sister comes into the room. Big Sister starts building a fort out of the 16-inch rubber alphabet tiles. The new grandbaby abandons the toy basket and heads over to assist Big Sister. Of course, the new grandbaby has no real concept of rubber tile construction, and her focused attempts at attaching the tiles while dealing with her wobbly ability to stand often result in a fall causing destruction to the walls so carefully constructed by Big Sister.

This frustrates Big Sister, until she pushes the new grandbaby away, which elicits terrifying screams of anguish from the new grandbaby. Jakelyn enters the picture to gently calm the little one and quietly admonish Big Sister to have more patience. Big Sister sulks for awhile, but before you know it both kids are back to building the rubber tile fort, although the new grandbaby has learned no new skills, and Big Sister still has to put up with her work being continuously wrecked when the new grandbaby topples over into the walls.

"That's entertainment," thinks Jake Lorenzo, private eye. I've always taken great pleasure in watching little kids struggle to learn basic physical skills. They are so persistent and focused. The new grandbaby screws up her mouth in a twisted look of grim concentration while she struggles with a new activity. When she finally succeeds, she claps her hands and laughs with joy, eyes sparkling with the excitement of achievement. Then she insists on doing it again and again, until it is imprinted on her memory.

Later that evening as I sip some Paradiso tequila, I think that in the wine business Big Sister is Napa and maybe Sonoma. All of the rest are new grandbabies. I remember being up here in Seattle 20 years ago when the Pacific Northwest wine business was an infant. Their white wines were acidic with generic aromas and flavors. Their red wines tended to be light in color and body with thin, over-oaked tart finishes. But they used grim concentration, persistence and focus, until now they have a real wine industry brimming with crisp aromatic whites like Hedges Fume/Semillon. They revel in inky, elegant reds like McRae Syrah. They delight with delicate, complex affordable Pinot Noirs like Willakenzie.

Many still worship at the altar of Big Sister erecting giant wineries of architectural wonder and filling these shrines with expensive, shining technological inventions. They desperately emulate Big Sister by pricing their wines into the stratosphere while pursuing the richest of the rich as customers and ignoring the working man and the simple wine aficionado.

New wineries popped up all over America. They struggled to learn winemaking skills, stumbled with tartrates in the bottle, and fought through unrecognized VA and brettanomyces infections. They focused on their own dreams, built their little wineries and developed their own markets, all the while mesmerized by the God-like abilities of Big Sister.

When Jake Lorenzo used to visit new wineries and talk to the winery owners, I'd get depressed. They had such good intentions and were so sincere in their conviction about making fine wines. They were like developers opening island resorts completely oblivious to the approaching tsunami of competition. I could see them headed straight for cataclysmic chasms because they had no real idea of wine stability or couldn't recognize simple H_2S, or thought, "If a little micro-ox is good, a lot should be better."

As I sit sipping this elegant tequila, I am reminded of the tenacity of our new grandbaby as she goes about learning basic skills. I am never depressed by her struggle, because I know it will lead to competency and fierce independence. I have a revelation. I now see that this is true of the wine business as well.

Big Sister and the Grandbaby

Remember when Monterey wines all had that disgusting vegetal character? They cleaned that up pretty well. Remember when Amador Zins used to have enough VA to remove nail polish? They've harnessed that horse and rode it to glory. Remember when Santa Barbara was better known for surfing and radical bank burnings? They've certainly turned that notion "Sideways."

Wineries have crawled, struggled to stand and finally walked on their own two feet all over America. There's the fine Lamoreaux Landing from New York, delightful Ferrante Winery from Ohio, more than adequate Messina Hof Winery from Texas. We even have delicious Gruet sparkling wine in New Mexico for God sake.

When new grandbabies learn their life's lessons, they gain confidence. They develop their own interests, interpret information in their own way and look for new roads to travel. At a certain point, their worship of Big Sister turns to respect that demands some competition. New grandbabies must define their own competence in relation to Big Sister.

When Napa and Sonoma were grandbabies, their Big Sisters were France and Italy. How the grandbabies worshipped at that altar. If Burgundy bought new oak barrels for their Pinot Noir, so did we. If their Chardonnay was stirred on the lees, we might as well do that too. If Bordeaux racked their wines every two months, we should as well.

Over time, Napa and Sonoma grew up. They began to challenge their Big Sisters. "Tastes to us like that lead pencil character in Bordeaux comes from harvesting under-ripe grapes," they hypothesized. "Tastes like that terroir in the Rhone is brettanomyces infection to us," they challenged. "Tastes like that funk in the Chianti comes from poor sanitary practices," they proposed.

At first Big Sister got frustrated and pushed the new grandbabies away. Over time she thought about it, realized that the new grandbabies were onto something and cleaned up her act.

The delightful thing about new grandbabies is that they have no expectations. All of life becomes discovery. They are born with indomitable spirit and a fiery tenacity. Give them encouragement and support, and they will clap with joy and sparkle with excitement over their private discoveries. They will come running to you on unsteady legs to show you their achievements.

Jake Lorenzo wants to support all of you. From Temecula to Monterey to Amador I say, "Keep on keepin' on." In Oregon and Washington I say, "A little rain never hurt anybody." In New Mexico, Colorado and Texas I say, "What are you thinking, but God bless you for thinking you can do it?" In Ohio and Missouri Jake says, "Tell me more, you're hard to get a hold of." And in New York, I just shake my head and say, "Well they're New Yorkers."

I want all of you to know that I respect what you are trying to do. I know it's hard, but the rewards are great. Please keep me posted on your progress.

A Day In The Life

Jakelyn's mother has created her own holiday. She calls it the "Un-birthday." Jake Lorenzo has no idea about the significance of this holiday, nor do I know why we celebrate it, but she announced, "It's my Un-birthday and we are going to Farm."

Since Jakelyn's mother always pays for her Un-birthday events, I was ready to go, but first I had to decipher the code. Farm. Is she talking about planting a garden of vegetables? I don't think so. She's strictly into her flowers and leaves all that growing of food to the detective. Could she want to visit Laura Chenel's goat farm again? No way, not since the French company bought it. Does she want to drive down to Stanford? That can't be it. She's not into sports and generally doesn't like red clothes.

Then it hits me. Farm is the fancy restaurant at the Carneros Inn. Part of Plumpjack Group, Jakelyn's mother raved about it after she had lunch there. She has me make reservations for Saturday lunch during Memorial Day weekend and insists I invite Chuy. "It will do him good to get out of his kitchen and try some fine dining," she explains.

So, on a cold, rainy Memorial Day Saturday we pull up to Farm at the luxurious Carneros Inn in our battered 14 year old Nissan. The valets descend on the car, careful not to rub up against the dirty sides, and open the car doors to escort us under umbrellas to the covered patio. We pass the oversized chairs and the outdoor fireplace and enter the swank restaurant. We are warmly greeted by the host who passes us off to the hostess who seats us and introduces us to our waitress.

The waitress notes that we have brought a bottle of wine and offers to open it, but we explain we need to order something off the wine list first. The sommelier brings the list and gives us a smile and slight positive nod when we order the Saintsbury Pinot Noir. Jakelyn's mother tells them we must have an order of French fries immediately while we peruse the menu, and I counter her zeal by explaining that we are here for a leisurely three-hour lunch and hope to work our way through their very interesting menu.

Hours later we have sampled a sumptuous Sashimi Tuna Carpaccio with roasted baby golden beets, basil oil and crispy potatoes. We've scraped up every last morsel of the Sweet Spring Carrot Risotto made with baby French carrots, lemon confit, marscarpone and carrot ginger broth. We were blown away by the Poached Petaluma Organic Eggs served atop spring garlic mashed potato mousseline with chervil and mushroom broth. We freshened our palates with the Heirloom Baby Beet Salad and finished with a perfectly roasted Sonoma Poultry Chicken served with smoked bacon, pea shoots, potato gnocchi, fava beans, English peas and a tarragon jus.

We sucked down the delightful Saintsbury Pinot Noir, reveled in the Altos Las Hormigas Malbec we had brought and enjoyed the Ben Marco Malbec brought as a complimentary comparison by the sommelier. Virtually every waiter, waitress, bus boy and manager had made their way to our table, brought a plate, removed a plate, changed a glass or explained a dish over the course of the afternoon. As we left, Chuy remarked, "That place wouldn't be here, were it not for the wine business."

The rain had stopped by the time we pulled into the Swiss Hotel where we sat outside under the heaters and sipped our Ghalarifys. The icy cold coffee drinks kicked in as Chuy and I walked over to Murphy's Pub to listen to local favorites Tuto Bem, and Jakelyn's mother went home for a nap.

From Murphy's, Chuy and I made our way over to Sonoma Jazz +. Held in an enormous tent just behind the Sonoma police station, Sonoma Jazz + brings in some terrific acts for a four-day festival every Memorial Day weekend. The audience is a great mix of locals and tourists, and every now and then the music is sublime. Chuy and I went to hear Trombone Shorty, a hot band of young musicians from New Orleans. They were smokin'. We stayed to catch some of Taylor Eigsti play his cool, cerebral jazz, but after Trombone Shorty's pounding set, Eigsti was too tame for us.

We opted to walk down the street to the Depot Hotel where chef Michael Ghilarducci's son has joined the fold after five years working in France, at the French Laundry, El Dorado Kitchen and Shiso. Turns out he has become fascinated by salumi and he's making his own. We tried a remarkable braseola and heavenly cured pork belly made with fennel seed and orange rind. We had a bottle of Prima Voce as we ate the salumi and sampled some of the other antipasti.

We took the bike path past General Vallejo's house over to Fifth St. where Jakelyn's mom picked us up and drove us to Little Switzerland. Tommy Thomsen had put together an all-star country swing band to help celebrate the tenth anniversary of his liver transplant. The music was sweet and the dance floor filled with couples two-stepping in grand circles, whirling and spinning as the mournful steel guitar wailed out into the room. At one point Tommy introduced a 16 year old boy who sat in and took two amazing solo turns before he left grinning to hearty applause and hugs from his mother.

Before the night was over we had run into more than two dozen friends along with several of the people working at Sonoma Jazz +. We talked and danced and drank cold beer loving the music Tommy was putting out.

Back at the house, the three of us sat on the porch with a nightcap. We had the new Tommy Thomsen CD playing softly and were sipping on some intense Zaya Guatemalan rum. We marveled at the breadth of musical entertainment we had enjoyed in one single day, all of it not 15 minutes from our front door. We talked about how it had been a day that expressed what Sonoma was as well as what it had become.

Farm with it's high-end, farm-fresh cuisine and Sonoma Jazz + with its high profile stars would never have happened here were it not for the wine business. Ghalarifys, Murphy's Pub and Little Switzerland have always been here. They are part of what makes Sonoma the small town place we love.

The wine business brought money, the wealthy and the famous. It developed hotels, bed and breakfast places and fine restaurant dining. It attracted people who bought up land, built giant houses on the hilltops and planted vineyards on incredibly steep hillsides.

Jake Lorenzo has railed long and often on how the wine business has changed. I complain about the traffic jams on Highway 12 and sometimes yearn for simpler times. But as long as the Ghilarducci's have a new generation in the kitchen, as long as Tommy Thomsen can find country guitar prodigies and as long as we gray-haired locals can boogie to Tuto Bem Sonoma will continue to be Sonoma.

Sure the wine business has changed and it has changed Sonoma with it. But there is no town without its people, just as there is no wine business without its cellar rats and vineyard workers. The people give a place or an industry its heart. Jake Lorenzo is glad to have his heart in Sonoma.

Holiday Culling

Jake Lorenzo loves the holiday season. For the most part, private eyes take it easy at the end of the year. Just like winery sales managers, who no one wants to see during the holidays, nobody's hiring detectives to dig up dirt around Christmas, unless it's Santa Claus seeing who's naughty and nice.

Although many of Jake's friends say that every day is a holiday at my house, our holiday season really starts with Thanksgiving weekend. The period from then through New Year's we call the "Days of Madness." People come to visit and people come to stay. Either way, there's going to be some serious eating and drinking involved. Life takes on a delightful haze when you spend most nights partying with friends and then, after sleeping in, you start your next day with a tequila sunrise, a gin fizz or some champagne. Once started, you might as well keep going, as long as you know how to pace yourself. Pacing is critical in the Days of Madness.

Day after day, night after night, meal after meal, bottle after bottle; the season goes on. Traditions develop and must be followed year after year. A great tradition at Jake Lorenzo's house is "Turkey Taco Day." The day after Thanksgiving becomes a sort of open house. People drop by and partake of the hundreds of turkey tacos Jakelyn's mother has fried up. We have chile verde, chile colorado, chilaquiles, enchiladas, tamales and a grand assortment of tasty incredibly hot salsas that Chuy makes special for the event.

Turkey Taco Day kicks off another event at our house: "Weeding Out the Wine Cellar." I don't know about you, but Jake Lorenzo is doing all he can to help wine depletions in this slow market. Annual consumption at our house runs about 60 cases, and that doesn't count the wine our guests bring to share. It also doesn't take into account that we travel 6–10 weeks a year. Still, no matter how much we drink, we are left with wines that may have exceeded their prime, wines that have lost their pigment, wines with corks that have ground to dust, wines that probably will not generate rhapsodic descriptions of exploding taste sensations.

This year I culled out anything before 1990. I know that sounds harsh, but 1990 wines are already close to 15 years old. I'm not terribly rigid about this. I mean I've still got a few bottles of the 1975 Chateau d'Yquem I bought in 1980. There's a nice selection of Port that causes me no worry, and for some reason I never mind having some older Brunellos collecting dust on my shelves, (especially since I can't afford to buy any of the recent ones.)

I don't have high hopes for these wines, but I've learned that one can never tell. All too often, some insignificant winery or some off-colored Cabernet has blown us away with its complex aromas, its velvety mouth feel, and its heavenly finish. Jake Lorenzo loves mouth feel and finish, and there's nothing like an older, perfectly aged wine to deliver the goods. The catch is, until you pull the cork and give it a try, you never know. Reputation, vintage, and vineyard don't really count for much, at least not in my cellar.

It's a lot like a treasure hunt, and detectives are good at hunting for treasure, because we respect the process. I don't pull those culled wines off the shelf, pop the corks and toss them to the wolves standing desperately with their empty wine glasses. Weeks ahead, I carefully select the aged bottles to be sacrificed to the Days of Madness celebration. I stand them up in a place of honor in my cellar. When we are ready to make the sacrifice, each bottle is brought out, carefully opened and decanted into one of our decorative decanters. The bottle is placed next to the decanted wine, standing like a sentry to its unfolding secrets.

After a minimum of an hour, we taste the beauty. If it is dead, brown, oxidized, skanky swill then we pour it down the drain, apologizing for waiting too long and praying that we don't have too many bottles of the stuff remaining. If as many, it is drinkable but unremarkable, we will pass it around expounding on what might be the cause. Underripe fruit is a common culprit, especially in conjunction with massive acid addition. Usually, someone in the crowd finds the wine charming, so we let them finish it.

But every so often, we hit a winner. In spite of the age, in spite of the brownish color, some of these wines excite. We offer it around discussing its charms, its depth and its flavor. We savor the taste and revel in the texture and finish. We make sure to save some to see if additional time will reveal yet more layers, and we thank our lucky stars that we opened the bottle in time.

Weeding Out the Wine Cellar continues throughout the Days of Madness. Over the years we have found food-wine combinations to help salvage mistakes. Let me give you an example. New Years Eve at our house is always a crab boil. Guests bring appetizers and we enjoy them with champagne. I prepare a large pot of dungeness crabs in crab boil a la a Cajun crawfish boil. We dump the food out onto a table covered with newspaper. Trust Jake Lorenzo when he tells you spicy cayenne pepper flavored crab is the perfect accompaniment for all those over-oaked Chardonnays you held for too long hoping the oak would eventually marry with the wine. Blow out your tastebuds with spicy cayenne and those over-oaked monsters taste creamy and rich with delicious vanilla notes.

You feel a sense of accomplishment when you deplete a case of oaky Chardonnay with your friends and 40 pounds of crab. Make that wine taste good with the food, and you are a hero. It makes you feel better about rolling up the paper, bringing out the red wines and settling in for a good night of drinking to bring in the New Year.

Jake Lorenzo hopes this holiday missive encourages you to weed out your own wine cellar. I know a lot of my readers are world famous winemakers. Surely, many of you are sitting on plenty of wine that would benefit from prompt drinking. Get to it man. Pull those corks. Decant those bottles. Taste that wine.

Of course there is a downside. There is always a downside. Sometimes Weeding Out the Wine Cellar only makes you realize that you will never catch up. The wines in your cellar are aging faster than you can consume them. Don't get depressed. Drink what you can, and send the rest to me. Chuy, Dr. Calamari, Jakelyn and her mom have offered to help me with the truckloads of wine sure to arrive.

In the meantime, have a wonderful holiday season.

Toonknockers

Jake Lorenzo is lucky to be alive. I have just survived a 17-day visit from the Gulf Coast Toons. Any Toon visit is a test of stamina, but add the complexities of this compacted harvest and you have a veritable marathon of activity that made me satisfied just to cross the finish line.

For those of you who don't know, Toon is short for Toonknockers. I can't explain what a Toonknocker is, but I would know if you were one. You know you're a Toon if your favorite dance hall is the center aisle of a bus, and your entire travel wardrobe has a one-way ticket. You know you're a Toon if you ask for and follow directions from a blind man, or if you come for brunch and stay for dinner.

Quite simply, the whole Toonknocker experience developed out of a relationship Jakelyn's mother and I formed with a couple from New Orleans. We met The Monsieur and Catherine the Whole almost 20 years ago. Delightful people, we formed a fast friendship. We shared a love for food, wine, good friends and offbeat social gatherings. We enjoyed music, laughter and travel. They introduced us to the wonders of New Orleans, Louisiana and the Gulf Coast. We showed them the splendor of Wine Country, Lake Tahoe and the Mendocino Coast.

Pretty soon we were spending a lot of time together. The Monsieur was a supervisor for a wine distributor. Jake Lorenzo was brokering California wines in New Orleans. It was a match made in heaven. We'd work together all day driving through the city, visiting accounts, and building friendships. Miss Catherine and Jakelyn's mom pitched in and we created the Waitstaff Ball, where we threw an annual party for all of the waitrons in the city. It was a gigantic success and the four of us remain welcome, honored guests in any restaurant in New Orleans.

Toonknockers

Jakelyn really liked them, and before we knew it, she had moved to New Orleans to finish her college education. We loved the idea. We knew she had someone there to help her, and it gave us more excuses to visit. We spent so much time in New Orleans that people thought we lived there. Even the Monsieur and Miss Catherine's kids thought we were relatives.

The hardest thing to do in a relationship is to find another couple to hang with. That rare situation where all four people get along makes for devoted friendships. When you find such a friendship, you must dedicate yourself to it. For the past 20 years we have spent four to six weeks every year with them in New Orleans. They visit us here in Wine Country two to four weeks each year. We have traveled together to France, Spain, and Italy. We have explored Mexico, Nicaragua, Costa Rica and Chile. We have enjoyed the charms of American cities like New York, Chicago, Denver, Santa Fe, and Seattle. Jakelyn's mother and I would rather spend time with the Monsieur and Miss Catherine than just about anyone outside of our immediate family.

In the beginnings of our relationship, we'd visit them in New Orleans. We'd be out most nights for cocktails, food and late night music. At least once during each visit, we'd arrive back to their house in a highly inebriated state and the Monsieur would say, "Have you guys ever heard of Arthur Prysock?"

"Sure," I'd reply, "I love his singing voice. What ever happened to him."

"I'm not sure," Monsieur would answer. "I guess he died."

We'd spend the next few hours sipping cognac, listening to old Arthur Prysock records on his turntable. To this day Jake Lorenzo still associates Arthur Prysock with early morning headaches.

One day, I was checking out the daily Jazz Fest schedule. Right there in black and white, it said that Red Prysock was playing in the Jazz Tent with his bother Arthur. I ran over to the kitchen where the Monsieur was waiting for the coffee to perk. "Check this out. We thought he was dead."

"Well," he replied, "if we thought they were dead and they come to town, we've got to go see them."

That became the first Toon rule. We saw some really good acts that way. Of course, we're going back a long time, so several of those acts we thought were dead, actually are. It doesn't matter, if they come to town, we're still going to see them.

After a few years, it occurred to the four of us that it was selfish of us not to share this wonderful camaraderie we had developed. That's when we started Toonknockers. We decided to hold an annual event, invite carefully selected guests, and slowly build a group of people who enjoyed each other's company and would pitch in to create events that would entertain us.

We tied the event to French Quarter Fest, a typical New Orleans festival held in the French Quarter featuring a dozen stages, hundreds of musical acts, and food from all of the finest restaurants in New Orleans. Jakelyn's mom and I would invite a dozen guests, and we would arrive for a four-day party. The first night might be a cruise on the river, or a simple meal in a local joint followed by a night at Rock 'n' Bowl. One night is a full-blown multi-course wine dinner at a first-rate restaurant like Bella Luna, Café Giovanni or Dakota. One night is always dedicated to a crawfish boil where the entire mishpucha, kids and all attend. Sunday we'll rent hot tubs at the local Baseball Park and watch a game, or go to some early evening cabaret. Somewhere in there is the bus ride, which is impossible to describe to anyone who has not experienced it, and a visit to the drive-through daiquiri stands.

We've now been holding this event for eleven consecutive years. We alternate between New Orleans and Wine Country. One year we make the trip out there and they host us. The next year, they come out here and we host them. We're very restrictive about who we invite to the event and have managed to keep it relatively small. We usually have five to six specific events during a Toonknocker weekend with 30-60 people attending each one. Over the course of the weekend, we will consume an average of 25 cases of wine.

Toonknockers could save the wine industry. Imagine if every community had a group like Toonknockers and what if they each had an annual event like ours. Not only would they be spreading camaraderie, friendship and fun, they'd be sucking down truckloads of wine.

And you know we don't just drink during the event. We drink during the planning sessions, the work parties, and the test runs. We make excuses for testing recipes, discussing napkin colors and making sure the wine pairings are just right. We taste flights of wine and do vertical tastings until many of us are horizontal. We have introduced dozens of people from Wine Country to the people of New Orleans and Louisiana. They in turn have brought dozens of people out to California to partake of Wine Country living.

Toonknockers

You attend an event where 50 or 60 people are having a wonderful time together, and you anchor that event around good food and fine wine, then those people are going to drink wine often to remind themselves of the event. They are going to return home to their families and friends and talk about the experience. They're going to share that favorite bottle of wine they discovered.

Jake Lorenzo thinks that people in the wine business need to remember how much fun drinking wine can be. Remind yourself. Get a bunch of friends together, plan some sort of event and pop a lot of corks. If you have a good time and you all get along, then invite some other friends and do it again.

The wine you sell may be your own.

A Traditional Recipe

On a crisp, fall evening Jake Lorenzo creeps up to the darkened garage. He turns the handle and yanks the door up quickly. The hinges creek, but then all is quiet. Jake peers inside the garage, trying to allow his eyes to adjust to the darkness. He hears a quiet thud, the refrigerator door opens in slow motion, its internal light a small beacon in the dark. Inside a 180 pound pig carcass, smiles a wicked smile as it slowly flops forward onto the garage floor.

*　　　　　　　　*　　　　　　　　*

Chuy Palacios, proprietor of the Burrito Palace, thinks that Jake Lorenzo worries too much about food preparation, especially refrigeration. Chuy and I are breaking down the pig for the *carnitas* feed we're throwing this afternoon. Personally, I'm glad I found that pig escaping from the refrigerator. As we butcher the pig here on my stainless steel table, I'm much more comfortable knowing that he spent the night in a cold box instead of slowly coming to room temperature on my garage floor.

Being a detective is pretty cool work, but the all day project of making *carnitas* is an art form that requires patience, knowledge and ritual. I love tradition and I'm fascinated by process, so cooking carnitas fulfills me in ways that running a stakeout on a sleazy politician can't. (Although Jake Lorenzo can give you a long list of politicians that I'd love to see boiled in oil.)

Like anything else having to do with food, one of the secrets to *carnitas* is cleanliness. I like my copper pot (*olla*) to sparkle. I clean it the traditional Mexicano way by sprinkling the pot with salt and then scrubbing it with halved lemons until it shines like Aztec treasure. Then I throw in all of the chunks of pork skin and fat that I've prepared, and start a slow rendering. Usually a few friends show up about the time I get a good boil going. I take the *cueritos* and drop them into the boiling oil. The thin strips of pork skin, completely shorn of all fat, cook slowly in the oil until they are tender. I fish them out with my wooden paddle, place them on a cutting board and cut them into chunks. I sprinkle them with salt, squeeze fresh lime on top and crack open the first bottle of tequila.

"This is the real breakfast of champions," exclaims Chuy as he samples the *cueritos*, takes a hit of tequila and passes the bottle to the next guest. *Cueritos* have a texture that puts a lot of gringos off, but I find that it works great with the salt, lime and icy tequila. It's also my favorite time in the cooking process, because usually the only guys to show up for the *cueritos* are the vineyard workers. The conversation is in Spanish, full of humor, teasing and sarcasm. As the tequila bottle gets passed around and beers are pulled from the ice chest, stories are remembered and tossed out.

I hear all sorts of stories. One grower is called *brasos cortos*, inferring he's so cheap that his arms won't reach all the way to his pockets to reach the money. There are lots of funny stories about winemakers, mostly about how tense and excitable they get during harvest. "*Solo es trabajo*," they say. "It's only work, why get so worked up about it."

When the second bottle of tequila gets opened, the *chicharrones* are usually ready. The crispy chunks of skin are popular and more guests arrive to get them while they are hot. I set them in a large pan, salt generously and then set about straining out the hot oil. The empty *olla* gets a second scrubbing with salt and lemon. Then I strain the oil back into the *olla*, get a nice low fire going and toss in about 60 peeled cloves of garlic.

"See," Chuy explains to the vineyard guys, "*El gringo maestro de carnitas* has secrets. He toasts garlic in the oil until it is golden brown. Then he takes it out and puts the meat into the garlic-flavored oil." Chuy helps me remove the garlic with a slotted spoon. He puts them into a bowl and seasons them with salt and lemon.

We put the chunks of meat into the oil, keep the fire at a slow simmer, and take turns gently stirring the meat with my custom wooden paddle. More and more guests arrive. The vineyard workers tend to get a bit timid as the crowd enlarges, so I'm encouraged as different guests make it a point to come over, say hello and have a beer. They nibble at the *chicharrones*, and try a clove or two of garlic. Jakelyn's mother brings out batches of tamales she's whipped together from the *cabeza* (head) meat.

Once the tamales are out, we start drinking wine in earnest. Jake loves a party in the wine country. Everyone brings more than a bottle or two, and the selection of wines is staggering. We have Sauvignon Blancs from Chile and New Zealand, Malbecs and Torrontes from Argentina. We have Shiraz from Australia, Cabernet Sauvignon from Napa, and Pinot Noir from Burgundy, Oregon and California.

Tourists are easy to spot. They feel the need to try everything, because they can't believe all the treasures that are being opened. Since they are unaccustomed to limitless supplies of fine wine, they fill their glasses to the brim, refuse to dump out even wines they don't like and usually end up as road-kills in the bushes. You can recognize them the next day, because their clothes are stained from wine the locals have discarded.

People who live in Wine Country know how to drink at a social occasion. They move from one wine to another, pouring a little taste and enjoying the flavor. They know the wine will not run out and that the variety will just keep increasing as more and more guests arrive. If they encounter a corked bottle, they remove it from the table, after confirming their diagnosis with another guest. If they get something that's funky with brettanomyces, over-oaked, or too heavy with vegetal character, they toss it into the bushes with a gentle flick of the wrist unknowingly splattering the tourist road-kills.

When the meat is ready, we use a small sauce pan and remove most of the oil. Then I pour in my secret sauce made with caramelized sugar, lemon juice and mezcal. It hits the pot and forms a succulent glaze on the meat. The chunks of meat are removed, chopped up and placed in trays. Hot tortillas, salsas, bowls of red onion and cilantro are placed on the table. People line up and are soon making tacos like factory workers in Ensenada.

Tradition and ritual are essential to cooking and winemaking. I think traditions last because they represent an accumulation of knowledge about the best way to do something. To make good *carnitas* you have to butcher your own pig, use a copper *olla*, clean it with lemons and salt, have ice cold tequila with the *cueritos* and use a good glaze to finish the meat.

Tradition in winemaking says you have to start with good grapes, ferment in clean containers, age in oak barrels, seal your bottle with a cork and give the wine some aging time before you drink it. There is a problem with tradition, though. Winemakers now have options. They can use oak alternatives instead

A Traditional Recipe

of oak barrels. They can micro-oxygenate. They can use screwcaps. Where's the tradition in that?

Jake Lorenzo reminds you that Mexicanos have been making carnitas for 400 years. They know what works. California hasn't been making wine for very long. Maybe our traditions are still being decided.

Window Diving

The Lorenzo household is winding down from the Thanksgiving holiday, which for Jake Lorenzo is a three-day event. Thanksgiving Day finds our motley extended family seated at two long tables where we feature my time-honored brined turkey roasted to perfection on the Weber grill. Jakelyn's mom makes a half-dozen delicious sides including green onion sausage stuffing, cranberry relish, mashed potatoes and coleslaw. Dr. Iggy Calamari bakes pumpkin pie. Chuy Palacios brings his legendary tequila flan and everyone else brings appetizers.

The next day I'm up early making salsas for our annual Turkey Taco Day extravaganza. Piles of habanero, serrrano and jalapeño chilies sparkle on the kitchen island waiting to get chopped into fiery, delicious accompaniments to the feast that Chuy and Jakelyn's mom will prepare. I crank out a chipotle salsa, a mango-habanero salsa, and a tomatillo-garlic-avocado salsa. I chop up the last of the tomatoes from the summer garden along with jalapeños, onion and cilantro to make a pico de gallo. I roast up a pile of chile de arbol to make a scorching picante salsa.

By ten, Jakelyn's mother is moving into the kitchen and we start cranking out hundreds of turkey tacos, fried to a crisp, golden brown. We make trays of enchiladas and more trays of chilaquiles. By noon Chuy joins us and gets a big crock of beans bubbling on the stove. He builds a giant pot of chile verde with succulent chunks of pork. Captain Jon comes in with his signature New Mexico green chile stew and puts it to a slow simmer.

We're usually done cooking by three, cleaned up by four and ready to party at five. Good thing too, because that's when people start coming. Turkey Taco Day is an open house. We never know exactly who is coming or how many people will show up, but we know at least a couple of people that we haven't seen for years will surprise us with shouts and arms full of wine bottles.

On Turkey Taco Day people come to eat. Guests go though our offerings like a flock of starlings devouring a ripe Chardonnay vineyard. All that eating makes them thirsty, so we drink. Bottle after bottle gets opened, passed around and drained. We used to unload all of our over-oaked Chardonnays at this event because the hot salsas neutralized the oak and actually made the wine taste pretty good, but we've long since used up our Chardonnay stash.

Now the tradition is to pour off older treasures that have been stored in the cellar for years or to sample esoteric pleasures from far away countries or counties. We keep bringing out food and wine as people come in, eat, drink and then leave only to be replaced by more people starting the cycle over again. By three or four in the morning we are down to the eight or ten diehards who will be spending the night. They help clean up, then we open the tequila and head to the hot tub.

The next morning usually starts late, except for the brief cacophony of expended wine bottles crashing into the garbage truck when the recycler comes by. I'm usually up by ten. I put on a big pot of coffee and start cooking our traditional Day After Turkey Taco Day Breakfast. When people stumble into the kitchen I give them a steaming pile of chilaquiles, I cover that with a couple of sunny side up eggs and then ladle on some of the New Mexico green chile stew.

We pop a few bottles of sparkling wine to help wash down the breakfast and before you know it we've sent guests to the cellar to start opening wine bottles and we're thinking about a late lunch. By Sunday, Jakelyn's mom and I are exhausted. We look at one another and ask whether or not we can do this for another year. Jake Lorenzo says of course we can. It's a tradition.

That's one of the things I love about the wine business. The wine business is built on tradition. Technology may or may not be helping us make better wines and science may contribute to better consistency, but tradition gives wine its heart and soul. Jake Lorenzo likes that Bordeaux varietals come in one shaped bottle while Burgundy varietals come in another. I prefer the satisfying pop of a Champagne cork to the quiet fizz of a crown cap. I find more satisfaction in using a corkscrew than unfastening a screw cap.

Does that mean that corks are better than screw caps? Not necessarily. Does it follow that traditional bottles are better than the new artfully misshapen, incredibly heavy ones that won't stack on your wine rack? No it does not. Should you infer that barrels are better than oak chips? You should not, unless your love of tradition makes it impossible for you to embrace a new technology in spite of its obvious economic advantages.

Jake Lorenzo loves tradition. That's why I like family holidays, New Orleans, baseball and wine. And I remind you that not all traditions are old ones. I have been involved in beginning more new traditions that most. The Cellar Rat Ball was a great tradition that lived fitfully over a 10 or 12 year period, until its hiatus due to liability issues. The Waitstaff Ball in New Orleans evolved into a wonderful tradition for nine straight years until hosting restaurants decided they could no longer be responsible for the carnage wrought by 500 partying waiters.

One of the truly great traditions of the wine business is the final Crush Party. I'm not talking about the one that the winery puts on for the growers and distributors and rich clients. Jake Lorenzo is talking about the crush party for the cellar rats. Because of liability issues and residual devastation left by celebratory cellar rats, crush parties are an endangered species.

A group of us independent winemakers still have one. In fact, we just had our 2006 crush party. We combine our crush party with a New Orleans concept called the "dine around." We move from one restaurant to another, having just one course at each, until we are sated. Needless to say there is a continuous flow of wine drinking, and while moving from one restaurant to another we will often pop into a bar for cocktails.

We started our crush party at noon. By five we were pretty juiced sitting in front of the Swiss Hotel where we invented a new tradition. We call it window diving. It its purest form window diving is a graceful athletic endeavor. Five hours into a crush party, it's a hysterically funny sporting event. Ray Kaufman from Laurel Glen started the tradition, but Michael Coats from Valerie's Vineyard perfected it.

As cars with an open passenger side window crawled toward the corner stop sign, our designated window diver would leap from his seat, run into the street and launch himself through the passenger window. Time after time, unsuspecting cars would roll by the Swiss Hotel. A window diver would burst into the street and leap through the open window, legs wiggling wildly in mid air. Patrons in the bar started cheering us on. Free drinks started appearing at our table. A new tradition was born. Jake Lorenzo says give it a try. It's not often that you get in on the ground floor of an ancient tradition.

WinePAL

On New Year's Eve morning Jake Lorenzo took a stroll down to Highway 12 to visit Jakelyn's mom's garden. Five of the half-barrel planters I had cut for her were strewn across the highway, cars weaving around them like drivers at Infinion Raceway. I dragged the planters to the side of the road and visited the mounds of gravel piled along the fence where I picked my blackberries and mounded all the way to the creek. Giant shards of familiar pottery dotted the roadside, but there was no sign of the plants or the smaller statuary that had once graced our backyard.

The infamous New Year's storm of 2005 capped a horrific year of natural disasters and wreaked havoc on our garden. The churning, white-capped rapids ran through our yard for hours slowly rising to the topmost step on our porch, but never entered our home. The waters knocked out three sections of our fence and dragged planters, gravel and pots more than 200 yards to the highway, but they stayed out of our house.

Funny thing about natural disasters: once the wind stops blowing, the ground stops shaking and the water starts receding, survivors go through a series of stages. At first, there's a stunned, numb feeling caused by the sheer force of destructive power. Sooner or later that dissipates and we start to rebuild our homes and our lives. But somewhere in that process we get pissed off. We get angry. We get mad. Sometimes that anger just sits, rumbling quietly like a sleeping volcano waiting for something to set it off.

Well, since Jake Lorenzo just lost a garden and not a house, I suppose that's why my anger wasn't too virulent. I'm not throwing empty wine bottles at FEMA officials and I'm not picketing county officials. In fact, Jake Lorenzo thought he was free and clear of the anger issue until I took Jakelyn's mom out for a nice meal to try to perk her up after she spent a day picking through the ruins of her garden. We sat at our table, briefly conversed with the owner and then checked the wine list.

That's when Jake Lorenzo's pent up anger spewed. Like a volcano lighting up the night, I was all over the waiter and the owner and anyone who would listen. The cheapest wine on the list was $28 and that was the only one under $30. It was also something Jake Lorenzo wouldn't drink unless someone was paying me a large consultant's fee to determine how it could be improved. There were more than 100 wines on the list at an average price of about $52. This at a local, neighborhood Sonoma eatery.

Our night was ruined. I couldn't calm down and Jakelyn's mom was incensed that I was so bothered. "You've seen this before. Just order a beer and let it slide." I ordered the beer, but I'll be damned if I'm letting it slide this time. I'm fed up with these ridiculous wine list prices and I'm not going to take it anymore.

I went home and called an emergency meeting of the Wine Patrol. Chuy and Iggy and Jim McCullough showed up and we railed against the sad state of wine lists. We spent most of the night sipping wines from my cellar and planning a strategy. We took a late night break for a visit to the burrito wagon, before we finished around three in the morning.

You need to know, Jake Lorenzo is not a glass-half-empty kind of guy. I've led a charmed, happy life and I try to avoid as much negativity as possible. That's not to say when I see a wine crime I will stand idly by and let it happen. Most restaurants charge way too much for a bottle of wine. When I can scrape together enough cash for a fine meal, good wine accompanying that meal is essential to making it a fine dining experience. Inflated wine prices take the pleasure out of that dining experience every time.

Why do restaurants charge so much, often three to four times the bottle cost? Because they can, because everyone else does and because we let them.

Well, no more. The Wine Patrol is pleased to announce its Wine Patrol Approved List (WinePAL®) program. The Wine Patrol will start deputizing people on St, Patrick's Day, March 17, 2006. Deputies will have packets of cards depicting the Wine Patrol logo and your status as a deputy on one side. The other side will list our mission statement explaining to restaurateurs the requirements for achieving the WinePAL approval and directing them to our web site to get details of our program.

When dining at a fine restaurant, one with wine prices in the stratosphere, simply leave a card when you pay the bill. If we get enough deputies to leave enough cards, restaurant owners will listen. Restaurant owners will scream that they *have* to charge these outlandish prices. That's a crock. They don't charge like that in Europe. The people would never stand for it. We shouldn't either.

If you want to see how it's done, go to Florida and visit Captain Charlie's Reef Grill where owner Ross Mathison has been knocking them dead for years. Every wine on Ross' list is priced at just $10 more than he paid for it. At Captain Charlie's, the more expensive the wine, the better deal you get. Corkage is $10 per bottle. Ross says, "I run a restaurant. I make money on food, but I love wine and I think the dining experience is better when my customers drink wine. If I make $10 profit on every bottle, I'm happy and so are my customers." That's why there are lines out the door most nights. Captain Charlie's Reef Grill is WinePAL approved.

Restaurant owners will sneer, "That's Florida, and this is California." OK, then take a trip up the Mendocino Coast and visit Meredith Smith's Mendocino Café. Her well-selected list has 40 wines mostly representing local Mendocino wineries, but with some Napa, Sonoma and Santa Barbara as well as French, Spanish and Australian dotted about. All but two of the wines are under $30 and more than half are under $25.

This isn't bargain basement swill. Meredith has searched for, tasted and bargained her way into an extraordinary list. "I take advantage of deals offered by the wineries. I buy lots of the wine and I age it in my cellar. When they go on the list, I take what I paid and double it. That's it." Indeed, it's Handley Estate Chardonnay for $23, Palacios Remondo La Vendemia Rioja for $22 and Andrew Murray Syrah for $28. By the way, corkage is $8 per bottle. The Mendocino Café is WinePAL approved.

We're not forcing restaurants to change their wine pricing policies, but we insist that they give some thought to their cash-strapped wine-loving clientele. The Wine Patrol thinks that every restaurant wine list should have at least one fine wine under $30 *in every category*. We think it is reasonable to insist that at least 10 percent of the list is under $30. We prefer that there be no corkage fee, but if there is, keep it at $10 per bottle or less. For each bottle purchased from the list corkage for at least one bottle should be waived.

WinePAL

The Wine Patrol would like to know who is purchasing the wine. Put their name right on the list, so we know who to congratulate or who to blame. We'd like to see creativity, selection and value in the wine-by-the-glass programs. We'd like to see restaurants take advantage of their location here in Wine Country to pass along deals offered by local wineries.

The WinePAL program is in the works. We hope to have our web site up and running by March 1, 2006. Go to www.winepatrol.com and then go to WinePAL. In the near future we will have WinePAL stickers that will be exhibited at restaurants right next to their Zagat ratings. We need deputies. Log onto the site after March 1. We begin deputizing on St Patrick's Day, March 17, 2006. The Wine Patrol rides again. Get with the program.

Vacations

The first of the year is always exciting for Jake Lorenzo, because that's the time to plan vacations. What with harvest, family and holidays, there is not much opportunity for a detective to travel after mid-August. That leaves the rest of the year wide open.

Most Januarys, we head to New Orleans. Ordinarily, January in New Orleans is wonderful, because there are no tourists. Since Katrina, tourists are hard to find at any time. This year was uplifting. Close to a year and a half after Katrina, most of our friends have either repaired their damaged homes or rebuilt their demolished ones. It was great to visit friend after friend and get tours of their new homes. I would gaze at freshly painted and decorated walls and think back to last April when I was drilling holes through the studs and pulling electrical wire. It was even better knowing that Jake Lorenzo participated in that rebuilding in some small way.

Restaurants and bars are going full bore in New Orleans. Tourist venues are hurting, but those restaurants that pull locals are doing great business. Restaurateurs who went out of their way to feed workers and citizens after the hurricane are packed. The people of New Orleans don't forget. They support those who helped and don't mind spending their money to do it. Wineries that are not in New Orleans working the restaurants, making themselves known, and supporting the rebuilding effort are making a huge mistake. One of the great wine markets in the country is desperate for help. Give it to them now, and they will support you for years to come.

Back in Sonoma, the cold, wet winter takes its toll. After a few weeks, neither the glow of the fireplace nor the warmth of a good port can combat the chill seeping into this detective's bones. And anyway, my birthday is in February, so it's off to Mexico for some R & R.

Some people on vacation are driven to explore every nook and cranny, visit every museum, eat at every great restaurant and view every vista. As far as I'm concerned that's not a vacation: that's working in a foreign place. Jake Lorenzo likes to immerse himself in the local culture, live like the locals, do what they do. Since it's February and I'm in Mexico, that means I'm at the beach. We sleep late, go for a swim, start cocktailing around eleven and look forward to lunch. Then we read, swim some more, continue cocktailing and look forward to dinner. It's a great life. Slows you down. Makes you appreciate life. That's a real vacation.

There are some hard and fast realities about vacation. For example, vacation is always better if the weather is great where you are, but sucks back home. (I don't know why this is true, but it is.) If you must watch your shekels like Jake Lorenzo, then you should vacation where the money exchange is in your favor. Right now, going to Europe and handing them a $100 bill, only to receive 70 Euros is ridiculous. That's why we're heading to Argentina in March where every dollar garners three Argentinian pesos. It's also why Jake Lorenzo revisits Mexico every year. Give them $100 bill and you get $1,000 pesos. Going to the money exchange in Mexico is like visiting a casino and hitting a jackpot every time.

Of course any traveler in today's modern world has to be cognizant of terrorists. Those are the bastards that have made it impossible to carry wine onboard planes when you travel. Hell, they don't even let you bring a corkscrew. Gone are the days when you could while away the hours of a long layover sipping on a lively Cotes du Rhone plucked from your carry-on six-pack.

Nowadays, our first choices for travel are wine producing countries. A trip to Costa Rica? No thanks. I'm headed to Argentina and Uruguay. A long trip to Japan? As long as I'm headed in that direction, turn left, and take me to New Zealand or Australia instead. Of course, there are exceptions. Mexico isn't much of a wine country, although they are trying and improving bit by bit. But I'm Jake Lorenzo, an expert on tequila and mezcal, so I'll make the sacrifice.

If you must travel to non-wine producing countries, Jake Lorenzo says you better come to love Styrofoam. I know it may not be politically correct, but before you get your recycled, save-the-earth, Sierra Club hackles up consider this: a twelve-pack shipper can go in with your luggage. That's right, you can safely pack up 12 favorite bottles and take them with you, being reasonably sure they will arrive intact, provided you use a Styrofoam shipper.

Jake Lorenzo has a couple of tips for you. If using a Styrofoam shipper, pull the Styrofoam out of the box and put in a big plastic trash bag. Then replace the Styrofoam and your wine and seal the trash bag. On the off-chance that a bottle breaks this may help contain the leakage. Another tip is to never sign your real name on the liability sticker. That's the sticker they make you sign that says you will be liable for any damage caused by your leaking wine to other people's baggage. Jake Lorenzo signs the name of his least favorite winemaker. Let them deal with the stained shorts.

April always involves a return to New Orleans. April means good weather, French Quarter Fest and Jazz Fest. Every winery should have a rep in New Orleans this April. Go spend some money. For May this year, it looks like we'll be back in Hawaii where Jake Lorenzo handles security for the Diamond Head Crater Celebration. If you've got to spend time in Honolulu, you can't do better than sipping fine Champagne listening to music in Diamond Head crater.

This June could be exciting. Jake Lorenzo has an offer to lecture at the International Bar Show in London. I would, in my humorous way, be telling them about security, hiring bouncers, and taming drunks. Because England is technically not a wine producing country, and because it is currently so damn expensive, Jake Lorenzo requires all expenses paid and a hefty speaker's fee. Our negotiations are dragging along, much like the San Francisco Giants and Barry Bonds.

When you think of it, wine is a vacation in a bottle. It provides an opportunity to travel to other places and foreign countries. It offers an insight into other cultures. It can exude a personalized sense of place. We can open a bottle of wine anywhere and be transported to another place.

If we are already in another place, then opening a bottle of wine reminds us of the best part of our daily routine. At home, the pop of the cork for Jake Lorenzo is the signal to relax, to let go of all the day's concerns and tensions. On vacation, a good bottle of wine is the reward we give ourselves for having the good sense to take time off from the hustle and bustle of the world around us.

Inspiration

The brain is a mighty tool, but no matter how much we study its function the genesis of original thought remains largely a mystery. What combination of experience, environment and imagination leads to invention?

Jake Lorenzo was pondering genius in Crabby Jack's, a lunch spot on Jefferson Highway in New Orleans. Jack Leonardi, who also runs the incredibly successful Jacques-Imo's had one of those epiphany moments. Boudin is the famous Cajun sausage that can be found all over Louisiana. High end restaurants make it with crawfish, or duck or lobster. Boudin Noir, Cajun blood sausage, can still be found in Breaux Bridge or St. Martinsville. The classic Cajun boudin made from pig offal, green onions, rice and spices is so ubiquitous that whole conventions of cardiologists salivate over the fortunes sure to come their way.

Most boudin comes steamed and is often eaten while driving in a car as a breakfast snack. Crabby Jack takes a smoked boudin, dips it in batter and deep fries it. There is plenty of fried food in Louisiana. You can have fried shrimp, oysters, cat fish or green tomatoes, but nobody ever though of deep frying boudin before. He serves it with a little green salad, and a side like French fries, potato salad or red beans. Crabby Jack's deep fried boudin is heart-stopping good.

So what is it that inspires us to invention? Jake Lorenzo finds that my most creative ideas come while I am drinking wine. Chuy and I were drinking Pinot Noir when we got the idea to hijack the Napa Valley Wine Train. A few friends and a Zinfandel tasting led to kidnapping Richard Branson. I know that those two stunts can't hold a candle to inventing fried boudin, but wine seems to be a trigger to creative thought, at least for this detective.

If that is the case, expensive wine prices may be doing more harm than we imagine. Who knows how many inventions have never been imagined because the inventors were too poor to buy a $140 bottle of Napa Cabernet. Personally, I'd be very upset if some greedy winery, and their high priced wine has deprived us of a solution to the energy crisis.

Thomas Jefferson said, "No nation was ever drunk where wine was cheap."

Jake Lorenzo has a corollary, "No nation has ever lived to its full potential where wine was expensive."

Jakelyn's mom and I have just returned from a trip to Argentina. I can't tell you the sense of contentment that comes from traveling to a foreign country knowing that I don't have to haul in wine for my daily needs. Going to a grocery market or a wine shop in Buenos Aires is like winning a lottery. Literally hundreds of wines line the shelves. Malbecs from La Consulta, Torrontes from Salta, and all sorts of wines from Mendoza to Patagonia call to the consumer. 70 percent of all the wine on those shelves is under $10.00 per bottle.

Stop in the wine aisle studying the various labels and a local is sure to come up and offer advice about what to buy. Their pride in local wines is obvious, as is their commitment to value. Most locals try to steer you away from the expensive, over-priced wines ($7 to $15) and onto something really good for $4 or $5. Porteños (residents of Buenos Aires) drink wine like they eat bread. It's just part of their meal, part of their daily intake. They don't have the money or the inclination to buy into hype. Porteños want a big steak, a loaf of bread and some red wine: the cheaper the better.

Jake Lorenzo is fascinated by the way technology infiltrates culture. In America, our individualistic spirit combined with our long-term capitalistic bent has convinced us all to own things. Everyone has their own computer, their own cell phone and their own car. When we go to a grocery market we expect to buy strawberries, watermelon and tomatoes year round. In spite of our air conditioners, our myriad of electrical appliances and SUVs, we scream like deranged cork salesmen when the price of fuel approaches $4.00 per gallon.

Other countries approach technology differently. In Argentina, where the culture is more communal, few people have their own computers. Instead they visit the local Locuturio and rent time on computers. For about 60 cents an hour, Porteños can surf the net, take care of their emails and search for information on their favorite wines. Stopping in a produce stand yields only local seasonal fruit. Porteños can use the subway for about 70 cents, take a taxi almost anywhere in the city for under $4.00 and have a great meal with wine at the finest of restaurants for under $25.00.

On the other hand, you can scour super markets, wine shops, restaurants and the black markets in Boca without finding a single bottle of wine from anywhere outside of Argentina. Argentines are proud of their country and they try to support it at every opportunity. They drink wine from Argentina. They like their home grown beef so much that they refuse to export it to other countries. They insist that they produce the finest cheeses, the best olives and the tastiest hams.

Most Argentines are fine with their government putting 100 percent tariffs on foreign wines, foods and clothes because they are convinced that whatever comes from Argentina must be better.

Try to imagine that in the United States where people trip over themselves to be part of the internationalization of commerce. If Americans proudly purchased Ford, Chevy and Chrysler while refusing to buy BMW, Toyota and Honda, the world economic situation would look very different. If America drank local and hit all of that Italian, Spanish and French wine with high tariffs until no one would consider buying it, the American wine business would be rich beyond its wildest imaginings.

Jake Lorenzo is not an economist. I'm just a private eye who likes to travel, but there is a definite yin-yang principle at work here. When people support their local products, the local producers prosper, but until people can experiment with products from other countries, they don't know what they are missing.

I love going to Argentina where I can sample hundreds of complex Malbecs, dozens of spicy Torrontes and dabble with Syrah, Cabernet, Merlot and Chardonnay. I get the chance to see how one country approaches winemaking and how that approach affects the varietals used to produce wine in that country. Yet, over time, I can see how that would get too restrictive. I can't help but wonder what Argentinian winemakers would accomplish with their varietals if they were knowledgeable about the French, Italian, Spanish and Californian techniques with the same grapes.

Inspiration

As a wine lover, I am charmed by the distinctions between Cabernet from France, Italy, California and Chile. I love the diversity shown between Champagne, Cava and Prosecco. It may be the detective in me, but I get a thrill over discovering new grape varieties from obscure growing regions in distant nations. I enjoy seeing how the various growing regions affect the grape varietal. I relish the differences in winemaking technique from the different countries.

It is a dilemma, but one with an easy solution. I'll just sample wines from around the world where they are available at a fair price, and I'll travel to countries that don't or are unable to compete in the world markets. It could be the best of both worlds.

The Argentines Are Coming

Spend five minutes with the news and you'll see we need to worry about everything from Al-Qaeda to Somali pirates to restaurant wine lists with triple mark-ups. We've got to monitor cholesterol build up, worry about our pets being poisoned by Chinese dog food and remain vigilant for salmonella in our peanut supply. Heavy wine bottles are under attack, screw caps may be reductive and lead glassware may cause us to glow in the dark. In fact, anywhere you want to look, there is something that will scare the hell out of you.

Jake Lorenzo is not an alarmist. I try to live my life without worrying about those things over which I have little control. Still, when this detective uncovers a threat to his countrymen, I feel the need to sound the alarm. I have just returned from two weeks in Buenos Aires, Argentina. Those people tried to kill me.

I know, I know. Argentina is a long way off and you haven't heard anything troubling about the place…yet. Remember, that's what they used to say about Afghanistan, Iraq and Somalia and those places don't even make wine. When it comes to Argentina, you just want to suck down those luscious Malbecs and not worry about the consequences, but Jake Lorenzo is giving fair warning. It's all subterfuge, a cover up for an evil plot to end life as we know it.

Their leaders are hiding deep in the Andes Mountains, bunkered up in towns that we haven't yet seen splashed on our news screens. Towns with exotic names like Mendoza, Cafayate, Salta and Lujan de Cuyo. Don't think for a minute that they can't reach us. They are organized. They are determined and they know where we live.

The Argentines Are Coming

Buenos Aires is the control center for the plot against us. That's where the evildoers experiment and refine their nefarious plan. Under the guise of tourism they entice citizens from all over the United States into visiting their gorgeous city. They invite us to see the colorful buildings of El Caminito, stroll the modern Puerto Madero and wander through the vibrant Corrientes corridor of theaters, bookstores and coffee shops. They seduce us with romantic notions of tango while neglecting the fact that the dance derives from prostitutes and pimps.

This is how they are: insidious, clever, subtle in the ways of charm and very, very organized. Get into a cab and let the driver know you are from California and the response is always the same, "Schwarzenegger!" they'll declare with a proud gleam in their eye. I don't know about you, but this unnerves the hell out of Jake Lorenzo. Most of us couldn't name the President of Argentina, let alone the Governor of one of their states, yet every taxi driver (and there are 38,000 of them in Buenos Aires alone) know to taunt us with one word, "Schwarzenegger." Who trains them? How do they manage to get to every last taxi driver?

When that driver lets you off in front of a great Italian restaurant, one like Amici Miei in San Telmo for instance, you have no idea that the jaws of the trap have sprung and you'll never get free. You move into the colorful room, are greeted warmly and shown a table. You and your friends are handed menus and a wine list. You peruse the list and, *this can't be true*. They have the Lurton Torrontes for 40 pesos ($11 US) and that's in a restaurant.

You order a baby arugula salad with perfectly ripened summer pears, festooned with crispy almonds and crumbles of blue cheese. It's divine and enough for the four of you to share. Then there is the house cured Carpaccio with greens, parmesan, and a thick, gooey balsamic vinegar that delights your tongue with perfect saltiness and the flavor of extraordinary Argentine beef.

Looking at the wine list again I spy a favorite; Preludio Malbec for 75 pesos ($20 US). I'm tempted to order two bottles and before we get through the Quattro Formaggi Pizza, the picture perfect Almatriciana pasta and the otherworldly Truffle Risotto, we have indeed polished of that second bottle. The food is so good, endorphins have kicked in. We order another dish, just to taste it and without our knowing have cleaned every last morsel of oyster mushrooms in truffle cream sauce so well, they really don't need to wash the plates.

Three hours later, we walked out of the restaurant having consumed three bottles of wine, six magnificent dishes (each portion of which was more than enough for four people) and two desserts. The entire bill for the four of us, including tax and tip came to $92 US. There is no such thing as a free three-hour lunch, but lunch in Buenos Aires is a close as you will ever get.

Just remember. This is their plan.

For 11 straight days we went to restaurant after restaurant to eat amazing food presented with impeccable service and were then handed bills that made us weep for joy. Most wines were well under $25 US per bottle in restaurants. In the stores those same wines ran $10 to $18 US, so we would drink them with empanadas or some of the delicious salumi, cheese and matambres available in the delis.

On our last day we took a taxi to the famed La Cabrera Parrilla in Palermo where we met another couple from California. The driver had just one word for us, "Schwarzenegger." We went inside to the warm, intimate, old-world charm of one of the greatest restaurants in Buenos Aires. We started with a Doña Paula Sauvignon Blanc to accompany the remarkable Hearts of Palm Salad that included three whole avocados, two tomatoes, greens and a dozen large thick hearts of palm. It was more than enough for all six of us. We ordered Mollejas (sweetbreads) and received a huge platter full along with a large bowl of French fries. Crispy on the outside from the charcoal grill and mouthwateringly creamy inside each of us ate our fill of Mollejas from the one order and washed it down with a lively Festivo Malbec from Michel Rolland's line of wines.

When we ordered the Tira de Asado (flanken beef ribs) our waiter congratulated us on ordering meat the Argentines like. Three large thin slabs of delicious grilled rib meat arrived and we tore at the chewy, flavorful meat until all that was left were the small bones and gristle. The Alto Las Hormigas Malbec was a perfect accompaniment. We knew we were getting full, but decided to order two steaks anyway. The Bife de Chorizo (Sirloin) had to weigh at least a kilo and the Ojo de Bife (Rib Eye) was so large that the waiter rode it to the table, dismounted and proclaimed, "Comen bien." We tried a lovely Lurton Reserve Malbec and finished with an elegant Cuvee de Los

The Argentines Are Coming

Andes. We were able to drain the wine, but gave the Roberto Duran cry of, "No más," with more than a pound of meat left on the table.

We finished with double espressos just so we'd have enough energy to push away from the table. This feast, in one of the top restaurants in Buenos Aires cost us $42 US per person. The service was excellent, the food divine. The wine was world class and the price went beyond value.

Are you getting this? The Argentines are trying to kill us. For now, they experiment on the poor, unsuspecting tourist who finds his way into some restaurant in a neighborhood in Buenos Aires. But how long will it be before they are here, amongst us, in the homeland.

Jake Lorenzo has trained for this kind of eating and drinking for most of my life. I have more stamina than the average U.S. citizen, but even I felt the need to have my doctor check my cholesterol levels upon my return. He took one look at my numbers, blanched the color of uncooked mollejas and fainted on the floor. He better toughen up.

The Argentines are coming. The Argentines are coming.

Unknown Wine Country

Downtown Montevideo has a gritty, unwashed feel to it. Like an old black and white film noir, the city pulsates with adventure, intrigue and the possibility of danger. Uruguay has captivated Jake Lorenzo.

Just a mile from the city center, heading north, you pop up out of the grime, like a ground hog on the first day of spring, to see the sparkling Rambla and the wide sandy beaches of Los Pocitos. Across from the beach, glitzy condos and casinos line the clean wide road. Hundreds of Uruguayans walk, jog and bike along the Rambla any time night or day. Even as you leave the luxurious mansions of Carrasco and head into the country, the feeling that Uruguay is one gigantic beach town is undeniable.

With over 420 miles of coastline divided along the muddy Rio de Plata and the sparkling Atlantic Ocean, Uruguay has attracted the rich and famous to its luxury resorts in Punta del Este. Yet, in its heart of hearts, the country remains a place of shorts and flip-flops, beer and chivitos, tannic wines and grass-fed beef. If the Napa Valley is corporate like Bordeaux, and Sonoma deserves its moniker of "Slownoma," then Uruguay is Venice Beach in the 1960s after an Italian invasion.

The people here wander the streets with thermoses under one arm while they sip their ubiquitous maté through their metal straws. Maté is the "Red Bull" of tea and Uruguayans drink gallons of the stuff every day. That's not all they drink. Wine consumption here is a marketing manager's dream of 32 liters per capita, compared to just eight liters per capita in the United States.

Uruguayan wine country is really a giant pasture that feeds 12 million cows while producing all that wine for its 3.2 million inhabitants. Uruguayan winemakers stubbornly insist on producing wine from the Tannat grape, one of the most tannic grapes known to man. With their ocean-based climate and the year-round rains it produces, Uruguayan winemakers struggle with both good and bad vintages. Maybe that's why they remain fiercely independent and go about making their wines in their own way.

A great example is Pablo Fallabrino whose Vinedos de los Vientos winery sits about 45 minutes north of Montevideo. Pablo has long blond hair, a scraggly beard, wears shorts and is always hoping for good surf. Pablo likes to cold soak his Tannat for three to four days, and then give it a seven to ten day fermentation at about 75 to 80°F. He egg white fines the wine, uses no filtration and no micro-oxygenation.

Over a delicious lunch, prepared by his gorgeous wife Mariana, Pablo told us, "Uruguay makes old world wines. It's one of the few places where they are still being made. We don't need standard wine everywhere. I like different things. I don't like to do the same things all the time." Pablo's been pretty successful. He sells all of his wine, exporting about 40 percent of it. Of course, he only produces about 3,500 cases, but it's Uruguay and nobody makes a lot of wine there.

Another day, we spent a long afternoon with the boisterous Pisano family. The loquacious Daniel Pisano took us to his vineyard and proudly proclaimed that his vineyard was located at the highest elevation in the Canelones wine region. He explained how this elevation allowed for the cooling ocean breezes to extend the maturation process and how it even helped dry out the grapes after rains. He spoke about the special terroir of this high elevation site and the character it gave to his grapes. It was an impressive oration, especially when you consider that this highest vineyard in Canelones sat at an elevation of no more than 500 feet.

Back at the winery Jakelyn's mother, Chuy and I were treated to a traditional Uruguayan *asado*. We dined on local cold cuts and cheeses, then sampled two types of intestine and finished with prime grilled beef. We tasted over 24 different wines including a Tannat sparkling wine, an intense grapefruity Viognier and a monstrous Reserve Petite Verdot. I mean, only an Uruguayan could think of sparkling Tannat?

Daniel said, "Our wines are half-way New World and half-way Old World. We have the ripeness and fruit of the New World with the acidity and tannin of the Old World." When asked how he came to be the voice of the winery, Daniel explained, "One brother is very good in the vineyard, so he does that.

My other brother is very good with the wine, so he makes the wine. I talk the most, so I am the salesman." Evidently, Daniel Pisano talks really well. With the help of his export manager Fabiana Bracco, they have made Pisano the number one exporter of Uruguayan wines. The wine is now sold in 36 different countries, but this is Uruguay so we're still only talking about a total production of 17,000 cases.

Jakelyn's mom opted for shopping on the day Chuy and I went to Castel Pujol to meet Francisco Carrau. Carrau comes from Spanish roots in Catalonia and exhibits a friendly, classy presence. Along with his brother Javier he also runs one of Uruguay's oldest, largest and most progressive wineries with annual production around 75,000 cases.

They have been growing grapes at their Las Violetas vineyards since 1930, but in 1977, the Carraus worked with professors from University of California at Davis to locate special sites for new vineyards. They focused on soil types and drainage capabilities and settled on a piece of land they call Cerro Chapeau. In the north of the country near the Brazilian border, Cerro Chapeau is Uruguay's highest vineyard at just over 1,000 feet, and in 1998 they christened a brand new, state of the art winery on the site.

Between their Cerro Chapeau site and their Castel Pujol brand, the Carraus make close to two dozen different wines. I asked Francisco about all the winemaking consultants setting up shop in Argentina compared to the paucity of them in Uruguay. He smiled and told me, "We invite the experts to come to the University to speak and to disseminate information, but we don't want some consultant's name on our labels. We must build our own story, so we need to research and develop our own information."

Currently, Francisco is working on an extensive experimental project to select the best clones of Tannat. They have isolated 35 different clones planted in Uruguay between 1870 and 1970. They also work with the UCD clone and nine clones from France. They hope to isolate the top four clones, clones that would produce smaller leaves to allow for more ventilation and looser bunches to help prevent mold. They are also researching the effects of different fermentation techniques on the polyphenols, color stability and tannins.

In this day of similar international wine styles, Uruguay remains a land of staunch individuals. There is no style in Uruguay. Everyone does their own thing. To survive in the domestic market, each winery produces a mind boggling array of wines. They make Chardonnay, Viognier, Sauvignon Blanc and Torrontes. They produce Syrah, Pinot Noir, Petite Verdot, Cabernet Sauvignon and Tannat.

Our experience in Uruguay was wonderful. The people were friendly, open, dedicated and enthusiastic. They drank and ate and told stories and laughed. We laughed a lot in Uruguay. Jake Lorenzo thinks that is a good thing.

Lorenzo Lavanderia

Jake Lorenzo walks outside from the Hotel Ermitage into another gorgeous day in Uruguay. Under clear blue skies, the trees in the lovely park across the street shimmer in the cool breeze. Just past the park stretches the Rambla of Pocitos, stretching languidly parallel to the Rio Plata. I gaze at the sailboats jockeying for wind in the distance and watch joggers trudge up the Rambla.

I'm thinking, "A cold beer might be just the thing to start the morning," but Jake Lorenzo is on a mission. While Jakelyn's mother slumbers on to her normal noon wake up time, this detective has to unearth a laundry to take care of the large bag of dirty clothes I'm carrying. Just two blocks away I see the sign, "Lorenzo Lavanderia y Vinos Finos." I'm no expert in Spanish, but this translates as Lorenzo Laundry and Fine Wines. I've never encountered a laundry that sold fine wine, and since this particular laundry seems to be operated by my namesake, I head into the shop.

The place is clean and organized. Plastic bags filled with laundry to be washed sit on the floor. There are four washing machines and four dryers. Finished clothes are folded into clear plastic bags, tagged with the client's name and stacked on a shelf above the machines. A young man, about 30 looks up from the counter. He has black hair, a thin mustache, a mahogany tan and an engaging, brilliant smile. He is wearing a tee-shirt proclaiming "Surf Uruguay," shorts, and flip-flops. "Bon día," he greets me in a mellifluous voice, "Lorenzo Lavanderia a su servicio."

I unload my laundry and find out that he will have it ready later that same afternoon. When he hears my name is Jake Lorenzo, he laughs and suggests that we might be brothers or cousins. Given the age difference I respond that it is more likely I'm an older uncle. We get to talking and I discover that his name is actually Lorenzo Lavanderia. "With a name like that, Señor Jake, I had to go into the laundry business, but wine is my first love. Do you like fine wine, Señor Jake?"

When I tell him that not only do I like wine, but that I actually make some and write about it as well, he has me step around the counter. I follow him past the washing machines to a door. He opens the door, switches on the light and with a proud grin announces, "Los vinos finos de Lorenzo Lavanderia."

The room is not large, but it is long. Two shelves run along the walls with another double shelf in the center. Soft lighting from sconces on the walls lends a warm cave-like feel while allowing enough brightness to read the labels. It is without a doubt the widest selection of Uruguayan wines that I have seen in one place.

I walk slowly along the wines. The entire double wide shelf features Tannat, the tannic misfit varietal upon which Uruguay has bet its future. I point to the Pisano, Pizzorno, Vinedos de los Vientos and Castel Pujol wines with which I am familiar. Lorenzo asks if I know the H. Stagnari wines, and I tell him I find them too oaky. He inquires about Bouza winery and I tell hem how much I liked the Tempranillo-Tannat blend.

We walk through his shop as he reverently picks up bottle after bottle, telling me about the delights of each. "This Sauvignon Blanc," he exclaims, "smells just like clean sheets hanging on an outdoor line on a warm summer day." He describes the tannins in one Tannat, "As stiff as new blue jeans after the first wash." An older, rare Petite Verdot he sighs, "It's as soft as a well-worn baby's blanket and as deep as a down comforter."

Investigation is what I do. When confronted with evidence, any good detective makes conclusions. I concluded that Lorenzo Lavanderia was my kind of wine expert. God knows, he has a unique descriptive vocabulary. We talked about the wines and which foods might compliment them. Soon he had a proposal, "Señor Jake, if you can wait for your clothes until tomorrow, I would be honored if you would let me introduce you to the pleasures of Uruguayan wine and food."

We arrived at an agreement. Lorenzo Lavanderia would select the wines and the restaurants, Jakelyn's mom and I would be his students and we would pick up the checks. It seemed like a hell of a deal to me.

I ran back to the hotel, where I anxiously waited for the clock to strike noon, so I could wake Jakelyn's mom with the news. "We're using a laundry operator as a guide to food and wine in Uruguay," she exclaimed. "You've been drinking the fabric softener again, haven't you?"

We got back to the laundry where Lorenzo waited for us with two six packs of wine. The sign in his shop window translated as, "Surf's up. Come back tomorrow." He kissed Jakelyn's mom on the cheek, happily engaging her in conversation. By the time they started talking about the healing powers of various Uruguayan crystals, she was won over.

We started at a local place called Pablo's Chivitos. Pablo himself hurried over to embrace our guide. Lorenzo told Pablo his clothes wouldn't be ready until tomorrow, and Pablo said it was no problem and led us to a table. Chivitos are the local Uruguayan sandwiches that start fairly simple, but quickly evolve into giant combo sandwiches. Each time you add an ingredient, the name changes. Pablo ordered Chivitos Canadian which had thin steak, ham, cheese, lettuce onion, tomato, egg, pickled vegetables, mayonnaise and mustard. In his honeyed voice he proclaimed, "Lorenzo Lavanderia recommends the remarkable Pisano Sparkling Tannat or the Pizzorno Merlot-Tannat with Pablo's Chivitos Canadian." Pablo brought wine glasses and we had a delicious meal complimented by delightful wines.

We jumped into a taxi and went to the Mercado del Puerto. El Palenque specializes in barbecued meats, but Pablo assured us it also had excellent seafood. Sommelier Oscar Carvajal ran over and embraced Lorenzo who explained the day's order of table cloths and napkins wouldn't be ready until tomorrow. Oscar assured us it was not a problem as he brought wine glasses. Lorenzo reached into his wine boxes and pulled out a Los Cerros de San Juan Gewürztraminer, a Castel Pujol Sauvignon Blanc and a young Pisano Tannat. He ordered gilled squid as an appetizer and a local fish called merluzza sautéed in Tannat, butter and herbs. The squid was perfectly tender with the tentacles stuffed inside the bodies and drizzled with olive oil. Both whites complimented the squid and danced with the smoky flavors from the grill. The merluzza was flaky and fresh and the Tannat and herbs gave it just the right amount of interest. Perfect with the Pisano Tannat.

From there we went to Don Trigo, a classic Parilla where we had olives, sausages, sweetbreads and steak. "With parilla, you need red wine, lots of red wine," exclaimed Lorenzo as he pulled out bottle after bottle. We had Tannat, Tannat-Merlot, Tannat-Tempranillo and Tannat-Cabernet. We had young

Lorenzo Lavanderia

Tannat and old Tannat. Clearly, Tannat goes well with grilled meats. As we left Lorenzo told the manager that the waiter's shirts would be delayed a bit.

It was a long grueling day and night. Lorenzo Lavanderia even sang for us at Tango Fun Fun and while his voice wasn't special, he more than made up for it in passionate effort. We got back to the hotel at 3 AM. Lorenzo apologized for ending the evening so early, but explained that he had work to make up for closing the shop.

We learned there is a lot to love about Uruguayan wine and food. We also learned that in Uruguay a three hour lunch lasts about 14 hours. Jake Lorenzo loves that.

Detective Work

Jakelyn's mother popped a guacamole covered chip into her mouth, took a sip of the ice cold Negro Modelo and leaned back onto her beach chair. "I could get used to this," she sighed.

A gentle breeze blew in off the Caribbean. The emerald blue water glistened as yachts slowly motored through the channel before opening up their engines for the short ride to Isla Mujeres. I dug my toes into the cool white sand, reached into the iced bucket of beer and opened another. "I have some issues, but it's not all bad," I agreed.

Ten minutes later, my beer was drained and Jake Lorenzo had to go to work. We had been invited to Cancun, Mexico by Darin Jones who was hosting the first ever Agave Spirits Challenge. I was one of the judges. We tasted tequila three times a day: at 11 AM, 4 PM and again at 9 PM. We tasted blind and there were 6 to 8 entries at each tasting. Tasting close to two dozen tequilas each day made for a pretty mellow vacation, especially if you added the morning beers, the afternoon Palomas and the evening selection of wine that Jakelyn's mother and I sampled from the case we brought with us.

The event was hosted by Club International, one of the Royal Resorts hotels. I've got to admit, the rooms were luxurious: two stories, two bedroom and two bath rooms with completely outfitted kitchens, all amenities and views of either the ocean or the beautiful pools. The maid service was so efficient that when they left our room we expected doctors to come in to perform surgery without any worry of staph infections.

The town of Cancun is a fairly typical Mexicano place. A bit dirty, with bus after bus belching black exhaust into the air, bumper to bumper traffic and festive colored houses, it still seems like Mexico. The hotel zone is another matter. A narrow strip of land shaped like a giant seven has the Caribbean to the east and a gorgeous lagoon to the west. Cancun must have once been a tranquil paradise, but that was decades ago. The Mexican government designated this quiet strip of land as a model for resort living and as a giant tourist attraction. What they have wrought is a smashing financial success. Today one-third of all tourist dollars pouring into Mexico enter through Cancun's state of Quintana Roo.

Now, from one end of the strip to the end, the hotel zone in Cancun has one giant resort pushing against the next even bigger resort, sort of like wineries on Highway 29 in Napa Valley. The main drag Kulkulcan, named for the famous Mayan serpent, lies listless as if spent from the hordes of tourists tromping its length. The dozens of gigantic resorts are interspersed with huge shopping malls and chain restaurants selling mediocre food and drink at truly astronomical prices, especially for Mexico. Try a $13 burrito that tastes like something from Taco Bell or a $12 margarita strong enough to be served at a local Alcoholics Anonymous meeting.

At night the strip lights up like downtown Las Vegas. In the heart of the zone are the pulsating disco bars with their scantily clad hard-bodied dancers, the flashing lights and the drunken revelers. Tourists line up for Bubba Gump's, Jimmy Buffet's Margaritaville and Ruth's Chris Steak House. If they are more adventurous they might try the Thai for its $19 Pad Thai, or Aioli for its Parisian priced French cuisine or even Casa de Las Margaritas for their simplistic, overpriced versions of Mexicano classics. This kind of stuff does not warm Jake Lorenzo's heart, even when I'm drinking agave spirits morning noon and night.

I needed a great dinner. I had to have some real Mexican food. Since the hotel zone obviously had banned any taco stands, burrito wagons or simple Mexican restaurants, we would have to explore Cancun City if we were to have a decent meal.

We sniffed around and found a Parrilla that specialized in wood-grilled meats and had a simple, basic meal, but it wasn't anything special. We discovered a seafood restaurant called Las Cejas tucked into the center of Mercado 28. It looked like the real deal: not a gringo to be seen, fresh, whole fish displayed in the glass cases and packed to the gills with locals eating giant portions of food. It turned out to be a local favorite, but who knew the locals like their shrimp cocktails sweet and their whole fish well done.

By our last day, I was disappointed, but I was determined. After all, Jake Lorenzo is a world famous detective. One of the other tequila judges was Elena Gamarra Hernandez. She worked at the University del Caribe in the culinary school. Her card claimed she was assistant to the National President and it also said she was Chef Investigador. My Spanish may not be perfect but Investigador means investigator and that stands for detective and she's detecting chefs. My private eye nose told me I was onto something.

I explained to Elena that I was looking for a truly wonderful dining experience, but one that was typically local. I wanted to sample Yucatecan cuisine made by Yucatecan chefs using local ingredients. She said there was one place I might like called El Pocito, but she didn't remember what street it was on.

"No problem," I said. "Jakelyn's mom and I will take you to dinner. We'll meet you someplace and we can all go together."

"They're not open for dinner," Elena cried. "So sorry, I have to get to work."

I wasn't giving up. We finagled a tour of the University that afternoon. Elena was about to show us the campus, when I grabbed her and pushed her into a waiting taxi. "Tell him how to get to El Pocito, or you'll never get back to your job." Fearfully, she gave instructions to the driver. I'm not proud of that moment and I admit it wasn't a nice thing to do, but I was desperate. I meant no harm.

Loncheria El Pocito is on Calle 31, Mtza 35. Manuela Uch Balam is the chef owner and she runs the restaurant with her family. The food is divine. We had chicken soup kissed with lime and chile, with crisp corn tortilla chips floating in the broth. We had juicy, tender roasted suckling pig with red onions, rice and platanos. Queso relleno was this fantastic concoction of local cheese stuffed and covered with a spectacularly flavorful ground meat stew. We also had a delightful platter of home smoked longoniza sausages.

They served agua de pineapple, de Jamaica, and de tamarind. They had soft drinks, but there was no wine or beer.

Yet this was grand cuisine. Wine could have accented and framed each and every delectable dish. Jake Lorenzo would hand-catch live iguanas for a chance to have a good Pinot Noir with that queso relleno. I'd fight live alligators for a good Syrah with the longoniza. I'd even brave a full room of snowbird tourists just to sample a moderately aged Zinfandel with the suckling pig.

Grapes don't grow in the Yucatecan jungle. Wine is not a native product. The foods of the Yucatan developed without the benefit of wine's subtle charms and flavors. It's a dilemma. What should you do when faced with a culture that has no connection to wine?

I know what Jake Lorenzo is going to do. I'll send Elena to negotiate with the owner of El Pocito. We're going back to Cancun for a long, delicious banquet and I'll bring the wines. Hopefully, by pairing her food and our wine, we can give Chef Manuela and her family an experience as wonderful as the one they gave us.

The Magic Card

"Gracias, a Dios," exclaimed Chuy. "Look at that sunset. I've never seen anything quite like that, amigo."

Jake Lorenzo, private eye, and his friend Chuy Palacios sat in the highest of four hot tubs on the pool deck as the sun sank slowly to its fiery finish for the day. In fact, they had most of the deck to themselves as the sky turned magenta and flamed to crimson. Jake poured another glass of the 1998 vintage Schramsberg sparkling wine into their glasses. Chuy raised his glass above the steaming bubbles coming from the tub. "To Jakelyn's mom, carnal, and to grandbabies. If she wasn't up visiting the new one, your amigo Chuy wouldn't have made the cruise."

Jake Lorenzo had been hired to accompany a small group of winemakers on a Mexican cruise. Each of the four winemakers was giving a lecture and running a wine tasting. In the lingering aftermath of 9/11, Jake had been invited along as additional security. Leaving Sonoma in the middle of a cold, rainy December for a sun-filled, 11-day cruise to Mexican ports made sense to Jake Lorenzo. The fact that Jake and one guest were on the cruise at no charge made everything much nicer. Of course, given the choice between a relaxing, warm cruise and a frigid visit to the new grandbaby, Jakelyn's mother opted to freeze her keester off in Seattle.

It had been a long day. Chuy and I slicked our way through rush hour traffic to the Oakland airport by shrewdly going in my pick-up truck. (Trucks get use of the diamond lane.) It saved us a good hour. But still the cattle call of airports, the hassle of shoe removals, and the crush of pre-Christmas travel can wear out an honest detective. Getting on the ship was a mess of disorganization and elderly disorientation. I took one look at the chaos in the boarding area, went up to an official, and we were politely escorted through the crowd onto the ship. "Have a good cruise, Mr. Lorenzo. Let us know if there is anything we can do for you." Security gets a lot of respect on board a ship these days.

I checked in with the cruise director, who welcomed me on board and handed me the magic card. (Nobody pays for anything on a cruise ship. They don't allow it. Instead, every purchase is charged to your room key card, and a 15% charge is added. At the end of your cruise, you get a 400-page bill that makes your phone bill easy to understand by comparison.) The "magic card" allowed me to purchase any beverages on-board for 50% of the retail price. Not only does security get respect; it gets a magic card.

Chuy and I checked into our windowless dungeon of a cabin. We met Edy, our Filipino cabin steward, and unpacked our clothes. We grabbed the magic card and went in search of a bar. We got our half-price cocktails and reconnoitered the ship. We arranged to be in the late seating for dinner. We located the various bars and restaurants, and searched out the new sushi bar. We asked for and were given a copy of the dining room wine list, which we always carried with us. The hard work done, we eased into the hot tub with our bottle of Schramsberg, which only cost $19 and watched the sun set as the ship pulled out from San Diego.

Cruise ships are not really Jake Lorenzo's cup of tea. They are floating bastions of nineteenth century colonialism. Lowest on the totem are the waitstaff, cabin stewards, and maintenance workers. Most are from poor countries like the Philippines, Croatia, Belarus, Jamaica, and the new Russian territories, and they don't make much money. The cruise director and his staff are primarily from the United States and Europe, and receive reasonable pay. At the top of the chain are the captain and his officers. On this ship, they were all Greek.

All of the crew sign on for contracts that run 6–8 months. They get *no* days off for the duration of the contract. They are jammed three to a room into small cabins below decks. Whenever they are working on the ship, they are required to wear uniforms and to be incredibly polite and solicitous of the passengers, no matter how obnoxious or idiotic the passenger. There are 900 crew members to service 2,000 passengers.

Their primary source of relaxation is the "Crew Bar," which is totally off-limits to all passengers (even cool private eyes from Sonoma.) The crew bar serves up discounted drinks and only charges a 10% service charge. On occasion, the crew can get a few hours off when the ship is in port.

The guests are primarily from the United States. On this cruise ship they also tended to be elderly with an average age of 60–70. Most tend to come from cold climates, have accents, and wear tons of gold and diamond jewelry. They expect good treatment, first class food and lots of it, and they like to dress up for dinner.

Service on board the ship was impeccable. Edy changed towels in our cabin every time we used them, often two or three times a day. He always had fresh water and ice on our desk. The beds were made promptly in the morning and turned down efficiently every night with a chocolate truffle on the pillow. Chuy really got into the truffles. Every time you pass someone in the hall, they smile and say, "Hello, how are you, sir?" Often they even remember your name.

Restaurateurs and wineries should study dining service on board a cruise ship. In the dining areas the service was spectacular. The waiters and bus boys were efficient, friendly, and expert. Sommeliers were knowledgeable about the list, helpful with wine pairings, and thrilled when wine drinkers made themselves known.

The list itself was terrific. It leaned hard on French wines, but had a good representation of California and other countries. Prices were reasonable, cheaper than the same wines at most restaurants. A delicious Mount Redon Chateuneuf du Pape sold for $38. Three very decent German Splatleses could be had between $12–$24 and made perfect lunch companions. The California section was dominated by Kobrand, but still allowed us to sample Benziger, Cakebread, and Domaine Carneros. Once you bring the magic card into the equation, prices become downright charming.

When Chuy and I boarded the ship, we brought along eight bottles of wine and a bottle of Centinela tequila. We drank all of that. After an eleven-day cruise our wine and liquor tab came to $424.00, and that's using the magic card, which gave us a 50% discount.

Jake Lorenzo thinks there is a real lesson to be learned here. Wineries should be giving their employees and growers magic cards. Now, Jake Lorenzo is a detective, and I know that many wineries already give discounts to employees and growers, but in the frenzy of allocated sales and waiting lists, many of the discounts shrunk to 30%. And discounted purchases were limited to sales at the winery.

With a real magic card, every time one of us went into *any* store or restaurant, we'd receive a 50% discount. This would be exciting, and it certainly wouldn't slow down total consumption. It would also enable a lot of your employees to afford to buy the wine that they make, but can't afford to purchase given their current salaries. Jake Lorenzo wouldn't be surprised if stores and restaurants participated in the discounting program. After all, right now almost everyone is hurting and "a depletion is still a depletion."

Think of it as a necessary perk for your employees, sort of a medical plan for the spirit. In fact, if you were really together on this, you could multi-task the magic card. On the ship, your card also opens the door to your cabin. Maybe winery magic cards could be flashed for police and give us a .04 handicap on any sobriety tests that we are forced to take.

Mother Nature

Captain Jon nosed the boat around the point of rock. He worked the twin engines expertly until we slid gently onto the pink, sandstone beach. Jake Lorenzo, private eye vacationing as first mate, leapt from the boat and set anchors, one after another until the boat was secure.

I hopped back on the boat, slapped palms with Captain Jon and gazed up at the towering cliffs. We sat in a narrow cove surrounded on three sides by sheer rock facings more than 100 feet high. Late afternoon sunlight set the sandstone aflame with reds and purples while casting shadows that highlighted the dark black iron cuts in the stone. The cool, green water slapped softly at our boat and I thought, "Life doesn't get much better than this."

Six of us were reveling in a truly deserved vacation. The New Orleans contingent, Jerry, Catherine and Miss Lisa, was taking a break from months of reconstruction on their homes under the direction of Captain Jon. Jakelyn's mom and I had just finished renovating the Toonknocker National Gardens, which had been ravaged by the New Year's flood.

We wanted to embark on a trip around the world, but since we were pressed for time, we improvised. We rented a 53 foot houseboat, stocked up on provisions and let the timeless magic of Lake Powell and the Glen Canyon National Park carry us where we wanted to go.

I pulled the cork on a 2004 Torrontes by Susana Balbo. Jerry grilled some succulent tenderloin while Jakelyn's mom whipped up a spicy chimichurri sauce. The boat bobbed in the water, the regal cliffs watched silently and "Caramba"…we were in Argentina swapping stories with gauchos looking at the Andes and arguing about the best vineyards in Mendoza. The intense Muscat-like aroma of the Torrontes filled the air and the crisp acidic finish brightened the chimichurri as we dipped our bits of meat.

Next, Captain Jon sautéed some fresh trout in a little butter and seasoned it with Herbes de Provence. I opened a 2004 Louis Latour Pouilly Fuissé. The heat of the day radiated off the stone cliffs and "Voila"… we were in France reminiscing about Paris and marveling at the Van Goghs in Musée d'Orsay.

I put on a pot of water and dumped in some spaghetti. I sautéed prosciutto, broke six eggs into a bowl and added lots of ground black pepper, while Lisa grated some Parmigiano-Reggiano cheese. I strained the pasta into a bowl, added pats of butter, the prosciutto, the eggs, the cheese and more pepper. Lisa brought the steaming bowl of carbonara to the table as Jerry poured a 2002 La Magia Rosso di Montalcino. The first stars of the night twinkled their greeting, reflecting off the still water and "Mama mia"… we were in Tuscany marveling at the red poppies swaying in the fields of yellow mustard. We talked of cobblestone streets, walled cities and Michelangelo.

Jerry went back to the grill with some CK Lamb. Catherine whipped up eggplant with onions, parsley, garlic and bread crumbs. I popped the cork on a 1999 Hernandez Ranch Merlot from Guerrilla Vino. The sumptuous wine and its nuanced mint character from the vineyard's surrounding eucalyptus trees matched perfectly with the fresh gamey flavor of the lamb and "Hey, Dude"…we could have been back in Sonoma sitting on our porch gazing at Jakelyn's mom's garden. Talk turned to the wineries and the town. We described meals we'd shared and memorable wines and reminisced on the good times.

We finished our feast, cleaned up the dishes and relaxed on the deck. We noted that none of the evening's wines cost more than $15 and that each was delicious and of its type and place. The night sky sparkled with stars. The moon rose and shined on the cliffs whose sheer size was somehow comforting, giving shelter to our boat like some loving grandparent cuddling a child.

For ten days Jake Lorenzo marveled at the vast emptiness of deserts, the simple grandeur of the Grand Canyon and the gorgeous red mountains of Sedona. I reveled in Native American history and studied the art and artifacts of a civilization that existed centuries before the birth of Christ. I was stunned by the enormity of Mother Nature's work, with her mountains and canyons. I was reminded of how little affect mankind has on the ponderous, inexorable march of the earth around us. Mankind is a remarkable species and we affect the planet around us more than most, but we're no match for Mother Nature.

When we work against Mother Nature we can produce some pretty unattractive stuff like smog, holes in the ozone layer and Las Vegas. That behavior angers Mother Nature who expresses her displeasure with earthquakes, hurricanes, floods and powdery mildew. But when man and Mother Nature work together, when we take the spectacular beauty of Glen Canyon, use our technology to build a dam and create an oasis in the high desert, then the planet smiles on us.

Wine is one of those happy confluences of man and nature working together to produce something special. Mother Nature toils for thousands of years to produce favored sites on the planet suited for growing grapes. The earth slowly and gently nourishes those vines imparting a unique sense of place and rootedness. We can't understand this phenomenon, but we have named it "terroir."

Man tends the vines, harvests the fruit and manages the fermentation. We cut trees with their own terroir, age and toast the wood and produce oak barrels. We make machines to bottle the wine, print gorgeous labels to decorate those bottles and spend precious resources to ship the fruit of our labor around the world.

In its own way wine is no less spectacular than Lake Powell. Wine is a gift we give to each other: man and nature. It is a magical potion that we have learned to package and distribute and share with one another. Wine is pure sorcery and its magic can transport us backwards or forward in time. It can deliver us to foreign shores or place us by a warm hearth of treasured memories.

We all need to travel more often. We need to break up our normal routine and put our petty concerns face to face with the enormity of Mother Nature. We should expose ourselves to history, different cultures and traditions.

Jake Lorenzo is trying to see everything I can while I am able, but I take solace in knowing that if I lose the ability to physically travel or if I lack the financial wherewithal to set off on a new adventure, I still have an alternative. That alternative comes in a bottle. Wine will be my point of embarkation. Wine can take me where I want to go. It makes Mother Nature happy and it gets Jake Lorenzo high.

The Dream

It's been a strange month for Jake Lorenzo. As much as this detective likes to travel, I'm not much for weekend jaunts. There's something so nice about the house and yard that Jakelyn's mom and I tend to spend most of our time close to home.

That we have spent two of the last three weekends away from home on short trips is unusual. Our first trip was to Santa Cruz where we participated in the celebration of our God-daughter's graduation from college. The quintessential college town, Santa Cruz is filled with young people sporting tattoos and pins through their flesh while they ride bicycles and use public transportation to get around town.

The graduation ceremony itself was relatively brief: two hours. The keynote address was suitably left-wing, and I especially enjoyed the angry shouts of parents protesting the speaker whenever she denigrated our illustrious president. Graduation is a time for dreams. These young adults are full of hope, ambition and high ideals. They are eager to get on with their lives and to see the mark they will make upon the world.

I was struck by the composition of the graduating class. It was about 40 percent white, 40 percent Asian and 20 percent Hispanic. Close to 70 percent of the graduates were women. This is significant, because these are the future wine drinkers of America. These bright young people are going to become lawyers and doctors and engineers and they are going to buy wine and determine who succeeds and who fails in our business.

Last weekend we went up to Amador Wine Country to attend the wedding of a friend's daughter. The area exudes a quiet charm. The scent of pine trees fills the air and freshens the hot, oven-like heat radiating from the ground.

The tiny towns dotting the highway speak of the past, of prospectors and gold, of timber and railroads.

Weddings are about dreams just like graduation, and this was a dream of a wedding. The bride was beautiful; the groom handsome. People ate from a delicious buffet and they sucked down ten cases of wine. This was in Amador County where the people have a gruff independence. They're friendly, but wary. They hunt and fish and grow their own vegetables, but there they were drinking all that wine.

I remember when the entire California wine business was about dreams. People dreaming of escape from the rat race. People intent on giving their families a deeper more spiritual life. People dedicated to making a joyous product with their own hands in their own way reflecting their own style. That was a heady time in winemaking.

People dreamed of having a vineyard, so they bought some land and planted grapes. It didn't matter that they knew nothing about grape growing. They figured they could learn. People dreamed of having a winery, so they built a building, bought some equipment and had at it. It didn't matter that they knew very little about microorganisms, chemistry, fermentation science and wine stability. They would learn as they went along.

People knew little about tradition or terroir so they planted whatever they felt like wherever they had space. They didn't know one varietal from the other, so they planted a bunch of them just to see which would sell the best. They used different kinds of barrels and blended uncommon varietals together. If you think back, they made a lot of mistakes and there was some pretty strange tasting wine around in those early years.

The truth of the matter is that people did learn, and in learning they achieved their dreams. The wine got better and more consistent. Decisions got made based on experience and science. The dream of having a winery took shape and quickly transformed into a viable business.

Once the dream became successful commerce, it attracted real businessmen, and then it was a dream no longer. Competition was fierce. Publications rated the wines and buyers paid attention to those ratings and scores. Wineries flourished, matured as business and frankly got kind of stuffy to my way of thinking.

The Dream

From my home base here in Sonoma, Jake Lorenzo would gaze at the expensive wineries with their picnic areas, their concert series and their summer theater. I watched prices rise until I could no longer afford to purchase most of the wines produced around me. I grew cynical about the entire business and thought that the times of dreaming in the wine business were long gone.

These recent weekend trips have taught me that this is not true. In Amador Wine Country people still have dreams. We stopped at a pretty little winery called Avio. Owners Stefano and Lisa Watson had a dream. They wanted to escape from their very busy lives in Atlanta, Georgia and when they visited Amador County it reminded them of their Tuscan roots. They have a tiny winery on 77 acres and are soon to release a Nebbiolo and a Sangiovese along with their Sauvignon Blanc and Barbed Wire Red.

As you leave Avio, you encounter a sign. "Thanks for visiting," it says, "please visit Sutter Ridge Winery next door." So we did. Sutter Ridge is another small winery on a fair amount of acreage. They make a dozen varietals including Pinotage.

A few miles down the road is Clos du Lac Cellars. They feature almost two dozen wines including Petite Verdot and Zinfandel. They have beautiful grounds, a very nice tasting room and they host weddings, including the one we attended.

I realized that the dream couldn't be dead, because all of these people were living it.

The dream exists in different stages in a sort of time continuum. I found these wineries charming. It reminded me of the early days in Sonoma and Napa when we all hung out together and drank each other's wines. Visitors in Amador can be infrequent, but when they arrive they are welcomed heartily. The wineries produce dozens of wild varieties, use all sorts of different barrels and may not be current on the latest scientific papers, but they are living the dream.

I feel like I've just graduated from some wine college where I learned that I can visit wineries around Sonoma and see sophisticated, mature businesses respond to winemaking challenges. I will likely taste consistently well made wines, but I'm not likely to be surprised by something new and different.

I can also go to places like Amador County or Paso Robles or Calaveras and see people just starting on their dreams. I can witness their excitement and nervousness coexisting as they simultaneously build a business and learn their craft. I can taste some pretty strange wines, but I can also be surprised by a lively Viognier or a bold, chewy Zin. I can join them as they move along the continuum toward becoming a successful wine business.

It's like I told Jakelyn's mom, "We're going to start taking more weekend trips."

Wine Deals

Jakelyn's mother and I sat at the Midtown Wine Bar in Eugene, Oregon. Sipping a delightful 2005 Chehalem Pinot Noir, we watched as wine merchant Tim Shimmel hustled behind the bar like a whirling dervish. He pulled corks for those wanted a bottle, poured glasses, explained flights for those taking advantage of the offerings and ran back and forth to Bel Ami Restaurant to deliver food dishes.

Typical of Eugene, the regulars were amiable to strangers and we conversed. One guy looked down in the dumps so Jakelyn's mother offered her plate of French fries. He munched on a few and confessed to being a stock broker. With a 300 point Friday drop in the market he felt the need for gin. Jakelyn's mother said, "I don't believe in the stock market. I keep all of my money in my mattress."

Jake Lorenzo, private eye, added while pointing through the large picture window to my truck across the street. "Yeah, that's why we have to take that bed with us whenever we travel."

The bed in my truck was in fact Jakelyn's mother's childhood bed. A mahogany four-poster, it had become Jakelyn's until she discovered futons. Now, it was on its way to Woodinville for our granddaughter. We were to spend five days with the grandkids, which is always a delight, but also a good reason to be in a wine bar drinking. We figured delivering the family bed would be a great excuse for a road trip to the Pacific Northwest.

Eugene is a town we've come to appreciate. Like everywhere else in Oregon, the people are just so damn nice. They are glad to see you, happy to serve you and more than willing to chat once they discover you're relaxed and looking to have a good time. They love to give restaurant recommendations and talk about the wonderful wines from the home state.

Jake Lorenzo loves the way wine is sold and marketed in the Pacific Northwest. It's really different from the way things are done in California. The Midtown Winebar, for example is a tiny place cut out of a huge old grocery market building. Three or four cozy tables, a wine bar that seats eight, a couple coolers for white wine and walls set like bookcases full to bursting with wines from all over the world.

The Midtown Winebar, which is not much bigger than Jake Lorenzo's living room, has more than 800 different wines. True, there are only two or three bottles of each wine, but I'd rather have variety than quantity in my wine selection any time. Tim Shimmel has personally selected every wine in the store. He knows about their back stories. He can tell you how they taste and he can compare them to other similar wines. He is, in fact, a real wine merchant, not some union guy working in a grocery market wine section.

Tim is creative, aggressive and inventive. Every Friday he has a free tasting focusing on Indie Washington Syrahs, or the wines of Antinori. From 4:30–5:30 PM and from 10:00 PM to closing customers enjoy $3.00 off the regular Bistro menu prices. That gives you a choice of three pizzas for just $5.00, a $4.00 Caesar salad and $9.00 crab cakes served with cilantro-lime aioli and organic greens. If you want a bottle of wine from Tim's shop with your meal at Bel Ami Restaurant the corkage is just $5.00.

The general consensus of Winebar patrons was that we should dine at the Chef's Kitchen. We made the five-minute drive with Jakelyn's mother's bed and met Bessie Bollag who welcomed us and handed us their wine list. "You're welcome to taste anything before you order it," she said. The tiny 18 wine list had Pinot Gris and Gewürztraminer from Oregon, Riesling from Germany and two whites from Italy. It had three Oregon Pinot Noirs, Barbera, two Bordeauxs and a couple of California Cabernets. Two-thirds of the wines were under $30.00 and all but two were available by the glass.

We tasted three wines before settling on a Casale Vecchio Farese Montepulciano d'Arbruzzo for $28.00. After dinner we went into the kitchen to talk to Chef Tommy Bollag. I asked him how he priced the wines on his list. "Simple," he said, "I take what I pay for them and then mark it up $6–$10. I'm a chef. I make money on my food. Let the wineries make money on their wine. I want my customers to enjoy these wines, all of which I tasted and picked because they go with my food."

Imagine a restaurant that makes its money on the food. What a novel approach. When I go to a restaurant I expect to pay for good food. The better that food is; the more I'm willing to pay. But these days so many restaurants simply try to break even on their food. They make their profit on the bar, the wine, the water, ice tea and soft drinks. That's why your bar wine tab at a good restaurant usually costs more than the food.

Jake Lorenzo loves and appreciates inventive and aggressive wine programs. There is a great steak house in downtown Denver. Once a bank, patrons enter through the gleaming bank vault door to be seated at their tables. They have an extensive wine list where all of the wines are listed at 2.5 times the cost, pretty standard in a modern restaurant. From November through New Year's Day every year, this restaurant sells all the wines on its list for half-price.

The manager told me, "Ninety percent of our business is local and regular. They come in here all year sampling wines from the list, but during the holidays they try all those expensive wines they usually can't afford. They know they are getting a great deal and we sell so much more wine during that period that we don't lose any money."

In New Orleans, before Hurricane Katrina, the Brennan family of restaurants including Commander's Palace, Mister B's Bistro and the Palace Café used to have Wine Week. Every day for one week patrons coming in for lunch would be treated to a free wine tasting at their table. The wines would be poured by the winemaker. Each day, each restaurant would feature a different winery. The hardest thing was explaining to the customers that they were going to get three or four glasses of wine to taste for FREE.

Even though Wine Week cut into their normal lunch sales of wine, the Brennan's made that investment to educate their customers. They knew that in the long run introducing their customers to wine and winemakers would encourage future sales. The Brennan's also hosted the participating winemakers and their spouses to sumptuous dinners to thank them for helping with Wine Week. In that way they solidified friendships and personalized relationships that are the key to continuing successful businesses.

My favorite restaurant in Sonoma is Chuy's Burrito Palace. The Burrito Palace has the best wine program in all of Sonoma. Chuy carries 30 wines, all of which he has personally selected. He marks up his wines $10.00 over what he pays for them. He'll open any bottle on the list to sell by the glass if the table will order at least two glasses. For each bottle purchased off the list, customers may bring a bottle of their own for free. Regular corkage is $10.00.

"Food just tastes better with wine," Chuy explains. "I make delicious food, but I want my guests to enjoy it, so I have lots of great wines at prices that won't hurt."

Restaurant wine prices that don't hurt. There's another great idea. I think I'll take Jakelyn's mom to the Burrito Palace for dinner. She'll just have to fetch a little money from under the mattress.